Sky Ta

More Stories from flying's Golden Age

Philip Hogge

SunRise

First published in Great Britain in 2022 by SunRise

SunRise Publishing Ltd
Kemp House
152–160 City Road
London EC1V 2NX

ISBN: 9781914489228

Copyright © Philip Hogge

A CIP catalogue record for this book is available from the British Library.

Typeset in Bookman Old Style and Impact.

Contents

Foreword

I have known Philip Hogge since 1955 when I was thirteen. He was a couple of terms ahead of me at school, and I think technically a year ahead in the academic system, but we both ended up in parallel by the time we left five years later. At this kind of establishment the house in which you live has far more social significance than the unrelated classroom life elsewhere, and his interest in model aeroplanes and a friendly, practical approach to life was a welcome relief for one who tended to adopt a tentative and cautious approach to his colleagues. Having become the man in his family some years before, when his father died, I can only describe his personality as mature beyond his years, with an inbuilt sense of helping others where the need is perceived, but never discussed.

We shared a study for the final two years at school and things looked up. Never in a million years would I have embarked upon exploits such as potholing and rock climbing had it not have been for his confident but careful assumption that these are reasonable things to do. I tagged along submissively and, despite the terror, did not fall off. Walking up and down Dartmoor and Snowdonia in the rain or snow also featured, and we both, separately, enjoyed the cadets' gliding at Exeter and Tiger Moth flying scholarships elsewhere. Had I been prised a little out of my shell, and slipped some of the surly bonds of repressive childhood conformity? I think so; thanks, Phil.

Parallel airline careers followed, sometimes with years of no contact, in fact the only time we flew together in an airliner's front seats was in 1980 when we went to Istanbul and Teheran in a 707. Philip Hogge was then training manager, 707s, and this was my route check for a return to this machine after nine years on the 747 and VC10. My memory, but not logbook, also remembers doing the 707 stall speed checks from the left hand seat during a test flight with him, prior to the captain checkout. Nothing wrong with that, and this sort of thing is right up my street. I must have been extra crew, and it was a generous and positive gesture from a manager who wished to make the most of his staff.

While still both enjoying the flying, travel and the agreeable socialising that went with it, our careers diverged again, by choice and suitability it has to be said. I continued a serious but fun relationship with Concorde, Antonov 2 and CAP10 in the twilight of my career, still confined in the tramlines of a personal relationship with the aeroplane and its control.

But Philip Hogge's progress in management continued to rise. Technical concerns remained an important part of this responsibility, but dealing agreeably and effectively with people from ever wider sources, specialisations and responsibilities far exceeds the boundaries of flightcrew imaginations. Within the airline context, the nature of a new British Airways formed from an amalgamation of two significantly different airlines gave rise to a host of new problems to be managed, ranging from employee to the political and diplomatic. I cannot comment on these from my simple crew viewpoint, and much of the subject matter of high office is a complete mystery to me and has to remain so, but this is the special appeal of his choice of writing — fiction based on a much wider-ranging reality than experienced by most of us. How real is it, and how much more is there to tell? We can only guess.

I once wrote a long and dense book about my flying experiences. Some readers were kind, but it's a weighty tome for heavy-duty flying anoraks. But where are the people in it? Philip Hogge's stories are quite different. They are wide-ranging in subject and cover a great variety of personalities, events and thoughts from days that will not return. The stories are short, clearly written and all about people and their experiences, good and bad.

Are the girls friendly as well as glamorous? Of course. The men handsome, competent and reliable? Mostly, but not always. But this is fiction, sometimes very close to the truth if you were there, and totally accessible to the general reader. What more could you want?

Michael Riley, BA Concorde Captain (retired)

Introduction

I was incredibly lucky to have flown for BOAC before the days of mass travel, when flying was still an adventure, passengers travelled in style, airports were pleasant places to visit, and the world was not at war.

The stories in these two volumes of *Sky Talk* are mostly based on true events. I have altered the locations and disguised the characters to protect the innocent, but they are all technically accurate, placed in real locations and in the correct historical context. Some describe the amusing capers of my colleagues, some are autobiographical and some are based on tall stories told over many beers.

But the thread of serious flying remains throughout. There is an aviation saying, rather trite, but nevertheless with more than a ring of truth, 'There are old pilots and bold pilots, but no old, bold pilots.'

Many people believe a pilot's world to be one of unique freedoms, a world where he can soar unshackled above all normal mortals chained to Earth. Indeed, there are moments when he or she is privileged to experience sights and sensations denied to those who do not fly. However, in reality, flying demands knowledge, precision and self-discipline. Yes, we were given rare opportunities to see wondrous things as we flew around the world, but in everyday life, they are also around us all the time, if only we take time to look.

Many pilots have an affinity with the sea. The sensations of sailing are similar to those experienced in the air. There is a freedom the landsman is denied, except maybe, when he stands on a mountain top after a hard climb. At sea, sailing close on the wind, the delicacy of touch on the helm is not unlike the precision required to handle the controls of an aeroplane. What makes flying unique is freedom in all three axes, but it is a freedom which must be enjoyed with great care.

Captain A G Lamplugh, a WW1 RFC pilot, wrote the following immortal words, 'Aviation in itself is not inherently dangerous. But to an even greater degree than the sea, it is terribly unforgiving of any carelessness, incapacity or neglect.'

Like many young men, I enjoyed risk – not blind unthinking risk, but the controlled experience of entering a potentially dangerous world while remaining safe through constant attention to detail. I was fortunate, when still at school, to be introduced to hill walking, rock climbing, potholing and sailing, all activities that have an element of danger but which, in reality, can be rendered safe by taking the correct precautions. Looking back, they were ideal precursors to the world of flying.

I believe there are four golden rules for all such activities. They are these: first, you must assess and respect the environment into which you venture and always — always — have an alternative plan of action. The mountaineer who ignores wind, rain or blizzard and presses on for too long is likely to come unstuck. The potholer who descends into the bowels of the earth without first checking whether thunderstorms are in the offing may find himself trapped by rising floodwater. The sailor who sets sail in the face of a bad forecast needs to be sure the conditions will not overwhelm his vessel. Similarly, the airman who fails to avoid dangerous winds, thunderstorms and severe icing conditions is flying before a fall.

The second is to know the quality and limitations of your equipment. In the mountains, it is your compass, map, boots, clothes, ropes and pitons. At sea, compass and chart are necessary too, but so is the navigation equipment and the seaworthiness of your vessel — what she is capable of, the condition and strength of the rig, the amount of sail she can carry in the prevailing conditions. In the air, there is even more — the structural strength of your aeroplane, maximum and minimum speeds, weight and balance, engine limitations, fuel and range, stability and control — I could go on.

The third is to watch and take care of your

crew. The captain of an aeroplane, like the leader of an expedition, must remain aware of the capabilities of his crew. All individuals, however competent, have their limitations which will vary from time to time. He or she may become exhausted or merely tired, suffer from something as simple as Delhi belly, or find themselves suddenly in an unfamiliar situation beyond the competence of their training and may need a helping hand. A good captain must remain aware of this, look after them, encourage them, draw upon the knowledge and expertise of the team, and conduct the flight accordingly.

The fourth golden rule, by far the most important, is to know yourself. Hubris and the temptation to show off has caused many a budding Icarus to fall.

It is absolutely necessary to know and respect all these limitations. If you fail to do so, disaster will surely follow. And they all apply, even in the relatively mundane world of airline flying. Respect these rules and the skies are there to be enjoyed.

I am an old man these days and people, knowing I was once a pilot, sometimes ask, 'Were you ever frightened?' to which I reply, 'Of course, that's why I'm still alive,' and quickly pass on to other things. However, in reality, fear is not something to be denied, it is the rational emotion that prevents us from doing stupid things. It ranges from mild alarm through fear to panic. It is panic which must be avoided at all costs, this is where knowledge and good training come into their own.

INTRODUCTION

But fear should be accepted for what it is — and respected. People also ask, 'Which was your favourite run?' as though I were a postman doing the rounds. But the more perceptive say, 'You've seen many things, which were the most wonderful?' Now that really sets me thinking.

Of human artefacts, the Pantheon in Rome and the Taj Mahal are high on my list. Also, Chartres Cathedral still dominating the landscape as, in the Middle Ages, all must once have done before being surrounded by high rise buildings. Or Palmyra standing alone and proud in the desert But, apart from creating Japanese gardens, mankind seems more intent on blighting nature with as much concrete and asphalt as possible.

I have been fortunate enough to see sunsets at sea, green atolls in the Pacific, icebergs in the Antarctic, the Karakorum from the air, stars hanging low over the Arabian Desert, ethereal curtains of the Aurora Borealis north of Greenland, the untrammelled beauty of the African plains and the mighty Nile wending its way through the Sahara. Thirty-eight years of flying gave me the chance to see all that and more.

But there are downsides. No pilot is a hero to his wife. While she has been looking after the children, running the home and dealing with all the normal problems of domestic life, he may have been away for several weeks, flying through the night and trying to sleep by day after crossing multiple time zones. He arrives home tired and crotchety, looking forward to peace and quiet only to be met with tales of woe – leaking plumbing, the car broken down, little Johnny in hospital having fallen out of a tree. These things seem always to occur when he is away and his wife left alone to deal with them.

She thinks he has been swanning around on tropical beaches eyeing pretty girls, he thinks she is making an unreasonable fuss. The very nature of a pilot's job has a tendency to turn us into pedantic control freaks. Social life may dwindle due to the vagaries of the roster playing havoc with the normal domestic routines of life — it becomes difficult to accept invitations or plan outings too far ahead — all because you never know when you will be flying again. Airline life is not always conducive to domestic bliss!

Yet despite the downsides, it was fun. I enjoyed it all immensely, as did my colleagues. These stories are not so much about airline flying as about the people who did it — their sublime moments, amusing moments and fraught moments; the situations they found themselves in when in the air or at play, their foibles and their strengths. And running throughout it all, the quiet thread of competence that made it all work.

I hope what I have written will give the reader a little window into the joys and vicissitudes of airline flying during those golden years.

Philip Hogge

Acknowledgments

Sometimes, in a chance encounter, one meets an individual who inspires a whole new direction of interests. Walter Wells, whom I have already mentioned in Volume 1, was such a man. I met him in the south of France where I now live; it was he who mentored my first steps in learning to write. Sadly, a few years ago, he died — I wish he could have seen the results of his gentle guidance in these two volumes of Sky Talk.

Many old friends and colleagues have helped and encouraged me with suggestions, and some have generously hunted down technical details and verified their accuracy. They are: Denzil Beard, Peter Benest, Nev Boulton, Hugh Dibley, Mike Dudgeon, Alex Fisher, Jelle Hieminga, David Hyde, Peter Kirtley, Gwyn Mullett, Alan Murgatroyd, John Richards, Mike Riley, Calvin Shields, Frank Tallis, Jan Thomas, Hugh Tweed, Keith Warburton, Chris White and Steve Zerkowitz.

Caroline, my wife, is my most severe and helpful critic. It is she who ensures my aviation gobbledegook is turned into intelligible English, my tenses and punctuation are correct, and proof reads my every effort.

Much of life is a team effort — I thank every one of you.

Philip Hogge

In the Windmills of my Mind

P at Ashford stood in the dark looking out to sea. He had left the hubbub of the hotel and walked round the small headland to seek peace and be alone. All he could hear were the soft sounds of waves gently sucking on the sand at the water's edge, the rattle of palm fronds in the coconut groves and the occasional plop which he supposed to be fishes jumping in the sea. Along the strand, intermittent flashes of blue-green phosphorescence came and went as each wave swished up the sand, retreated, swished again, withdrew and continued swishing in a slow, sleepy rhythm. With eyes now fully accustomed to the dark, he could see, by starlight alone, the long strip of white coral sand that lay between him and the ocean. Beyond it, reflected in the water, even more stars swayed in harmony as each wave slid towards him. Above, motionless in the heavens, and surrounded by diamonds, the great swathe of the Milky Way stretched from the horizon towards the palm trees behind him — so tranquil, so infinite, far exceeding the vastness of the ocean before him.

He stood in wonder, entranced. Then, since no one else was around, he stripped off his clothes and walked to where the phosphorescence glowed in the dark. His feet and toes were immediately outlined in a myriad of lights. Water falling from his cupped hands looked like aquamarines pouring into the sea. He felt as though he had plunged his arms into a treasure chest of jewels. He swam a few yards out to sea, rolled onto his back and floated in space, suspended between the stars above and the jewels beneath.

He let his mind drift to other moments when he had felt an equal oneness with the natural world. The first was as a small boy, lying in a field listening to the hum of insects in flowers and grass, watching buzzards circling and calling overhead. He had felt it again when sailing at night, south of Ireland, well away from the busy shipping lanes of the English Channel, the only lights being the stars above and the comforting loom of a distant lighthouse flashing its signal every five seconds. Alone at the helm, with the others asleep down below, and the sea unusually calm, he felt he could touch the infinite.

Reluctantly, he swam back to the shore, found the bench where he had left his clothes and sat for a while, drying slowly in the velvet night air before dressing and returning to his room. The hotel was quieter now. He showered off the salt, slipped into bed, hoping soon to fall asleep. But his mind kept flying round the world to other enchanted moments: sitting high on a mountain ridge in Scotland watching clouds catch fire in the setting sun; standing on the escarpment of the Rift Valley in Kenya gazing across the silent expanse of grasslands stretching to the far horizon; feeling a sudden chill in the Arabian desert after the sun had disappeared leaving the stars hanging low in the night sky; and sitting in a small yacht suspended in a breathless pink bubble of vapour, the sea and sky totally obscured — nothing to be seen but pink — no division between air and water, until the rising sun gradually dispersed the mist, changing all to dove grey, then white and finally to blue.

But it was not only the infinite that enthralled him, it was the minutiae too. Wordsworth knew it: 'Getting and spending, we lay waste our powers' — how often, in our busy lives, do we stop and really observe? The beauty of a fallen leaf, mossy patterns on stones, silver trunks of beech trees in a forest standing like cathedral columns, multi-coloured iridescence on the backs of beetles, the corn in fields flowing like waves in the wind. People love flowers, but do they ever stop to admire the golden eyes of a toad? Orwell did!

He looked at his watch; still only ten o'clock: 'Call time's at six, I need to sleep. Tomorrow will be a long day — Barbados, Manaus and back'. He rang reception to make sure he would be called at the right time.

His thoughts whirled again, this time to the beauties of Newtonian physics — the Moon in orbit around the Earth, the planets around the Sun, and the whole Solar System, part of the Milky Way, in a swirling arm of our galaxy. How many more galaxies are there in the infinity of space? How was the universe made? All the elements and minerals on Earth, the organic compounds in every living thing and in our own bodies? We are all made of star dust. Evolution is a fact, not merely a theory, but what started it all? Did the Big Bang really happen? How did life begin? He was not a religious man, but was it just an accident of chemistry or a divine spark? And why is it all so beautiful?

The telephone rang, 'It's six o'clock captain, your pick-up is at seven.' As he struggled back to consciousness and came down to Earth, he tried in vain to hold on to that image of earthrise, the one taken by the Apollo astronauts: 'I must have been dreaming'. The image fades. 'Have I given my heart away? Now I must be practical — ready to face the day.'

Right — shower, dress and pack; Manaus, here we come! This flight's going to be fun. Never been to Manaus before. New route. Special charter for a group of tourists joining a cruise ship for a voyage down the Amazon. A two-hour wait on the ground for the group coming off the ship, then back to Barbados. He would fly it down. Andy, his co-pilot, would fly it back.

Downstairs, he found the crew gathering in the foyer around a side table with pots of coffee and trays of sandwiches laid out for them by the hotel. They were all a little excited. What a shame there'd be no time for sightseeing.

At flight briefing, they went through their usual routine — flight plan checked, weather good, only a few thunderstorms near Trinidad, and then fair weather cumulus with clear skies at Manaus. The route was straightforward enough, take-off on runway 09, turn south towards Port of Spain in Trinidad, and from there due south over El Calleo in Venezuela, then Boa Vista in Brazil and on to Manaus. 'Piece of cake,' as they used to say.

The few scattered thunderstorms were no trouble at all. He weaved between them, keeping well clear of their white castellated tops. Proteus rising from the sea? No — more like Zeus with his many thunderbolts. He knew the deadly powers hidden within — vicious winds, tornadoes, ice and hail. But ahead, the skies were clear, the flying easy. Down below, after passing some curious flat-topped mountains in the highlands of eastern Venezuela, the land stretched before him from horizon to horizon in a flat infinity of green. Pat let his mind wander again: 'What are those mountain tops? They are certainly unusual; how many species live down there I wonder?'

Trees, plants, animals, birds, fishes, snakes, reptiles and quantities of insects, filling every niche in the environment. Primitive peoples, perhaps, unknown to civilisation. How do they view their world? What belief systems do they have? Are they animists, believing spirits inhabit every rock, spring and pool? Do they worship animals and ancient trees, thinking they all have souls?

He pondered again the beauty of all these life forms, even poisonous snakes and crocodiles (or are they caimans?) have their place. How much is ruled by mathematics rather than biology? The Fibonacci Sequence for example, whose simple numbers describe the spirals of sea shells, the pattern of seeds in sunflowers, the scales on fir cones, the distribution of leaves on plants. Do they also describe the whirls of soap suds going down a plug hole, the clouds around a hurricane or the arms of a galaxy? Probably not! 'I wonder what my passengers would say if they thought their captain was dreaming on the job'. But Pat knew from long experience that flying consists of many contrasts. That is one of its beauties. There are times of intense concentration and times, as now, when one can relax. The trick is to know which is which and to remain alert for the unexpected. Contemplating such things kept him alert, especially in the dead of night.

Many were the times he had gazed out of the cockpit windows at mountains and glaciers in the Karakorum, ice caps and icebergs in Greenland, multiple lakes in northern Canada, thousands of miles of frozen tundra in Siberia, dried-up water courses in the Sahara, huge cauliflower thunderheads over central Africa, the intense blue of the Indian Ocean, the Aurora Borealis and the stars at dead of night. But never before had he seen such an infinity of rainforest.

OK — time to concentrate! Thirty minutes before top of descent, he read through the notes he had made before leaving London three days before, reminded himself of the salient points, looked once more through the instrument approach charts for the Eduardo Gomes International Airport which lay on the north-western edge of the city, then briefed his crew.

130 miles out, they started down, he could see the Rio Negro on the right-hand side and, as they came closer, the city of Manaus on its north bank near the confluence with the Amazon. The river was aptly named, its waters almost black, whereas the silty waters of the Amazon were a milky chocolate brown. ATC cleared them to descend to 2,000 feet, 'Call the field in sight.' As they neared the city, Pat saw the airfield ahead and to the left, he asked for a visual approach, banked the aircraft towards the runway, lined up on the approach, landed, let it roll to the far end and turned off onto the taxiway that led towards the low white terminal buildings. Apart from

some abandoned aircraft left to rot in the steaming heat of the tropical rainforest, the airport looked like any other.

After the passengers left, the aircraft was surrounded by the usual chaos of baggage carts, fuel bowsers and vans of every sort, cleaners swarmed through the cabins, bags of rubbish were taken out, catering supplies came on board and carefully stowed away — all under the watchful eyes of the cabin crew. Gordon, the flight engineer, went out onto the tarmac to supervise the refuelling and check the outside of the aircraft. Pat walked over to the ATC offices in the terminal to report their arrival and ensure that their flight plan back to Barbados was filed correctly with the authorities, while Andy stayed in the cockpit, setting the flight instruments and navigation systems to his liking. The bustle of activity slowed, then ceased and they waited. Where were the passengers? Delayed at the docks, they were told. Pat said they had better come soon, or the crew would run out of hours, and began looking through a guidebook he had picked up in the terminal. Suddenly he realised what those flat-topped mountains were, the ones he had seen on the way down, The Lost World of Conan Doyle. He showed it to Andy, who wasn't much interested, and decided to look out for them as they flew north.

It was mid-afternoon when the passengers eventually arrived. With all this time wasted on the ground, it would be dark when they landed in Barbados. After everyone had boarded, they took off and flew back along the same route down which they had flown that morning. More clouds had developed during the day, but through the many gaps Pat could still see the green tropical rainforest below and the odd glint of sun on the Rio Branco out to his left. He searched the land ahead, looking for those mountains he longed to see — mesas in geological terms, Tepuis in the local language — but the clouds hiding Boa Vista below stretched solidly north. Will they cover the mountains too? He hoped not.

Then he saw them — great monoliths, wreathed in mist, their flat tabletops separated by vertical cliffs from the surrounding blanket of solid white cloud. There were several. He had thought there would only be one. Which one is Mount Roraima? The lost world? Is it the triangular one over there? His guidebook gave little help, all the photos having been taken at ground level. Somewhere down there were the Angel Falls, he looked but couldn't see them. He remembered reading about Professor Challenger in Conan Doyle's book when he was a child. Dinosaurs and other creatures bypassed by evolution. It all looked so unreal, what animals and plants live there now? No dinosaurs or pterodactyls, more's the pity. No ape-men either. He vowed to read The Lost World again and look up the geology and history of these mysterious unearthly mountains when he got home.

Nearing Trinidad, Pat could see the thunderclouds ahead, the same ones they had negotiated coming south that morning. Now they were even higher, having grown more massive in the heat of the day. But they were still widely scattered and he knew Andy would easily bypass them with only a few small deviations off course. How magnificent they were! Their anvil tops lit bright in the setting sun. The ground barely visible in the soft purple-brown haze. Hidden below the horizon on his left, the sun cast a long shadow slanting up through the atmosphere, leaving the body of the clouds beneath, dark under their golden caps. The shadow of the Earth through the atmosphere. Clear proof the world was round: so much for the Flat Earthers!

It was dark as Andy started their descent towards Barbados. Time to concentrate again. Far ahead Pat could just make out the lights of Bridgetown on the west coast of the island and the airport to the southeast. Andy slowed the aircraft, asked for the flaps and then the undercarriage to be lowered, steadied it on the approach, flew down towards the runway and gently touched it down at exactly the right speed and in exactly the right place — as the good book demanded. What a perfect end to a perfect day. 'Well done, Andy, nice one.'

On the bus to the hotel, he thanked his crew for a job well done. Their passengers were happy with the cruise up the Amazon and looking forward to going home. That night, as he lay in bed, the setting moon still visible outside his bedroom window, he let his mind free wheel once more. What a wonderful day it had been. So many things to see and ponder. Does the jungle also bare its bosom to the moon? His inner voice often led him down strange paths: 'I hope I didn't talk out loud; my crew might think me very odd if they could see the windmills of my mind.'

The world is too much with us; late and soon,
Getting and spending, we lay waste our powers:
Little we see in Nature that is ours;
We have given our hearts away, a sordid boon!
This Sea that bares her bosom to the moon;
The winds that will be howling at all hours,
And are up-gathered now like sleeping flowers;
For this, for everything, we are out of tune;
It moves us not. Great God! I'd rather be
A Pagan suckled in a creed outworn;
So might I, standing on this pleasant lea,
Have glimpses that would make me less forlorn;

SKY TALK 2

Have sight of Proteus rising from the sea;
Or hear old Triton blow his wreathèd horn.

William Wordsworth 1802

The One That Got Away

Captain Thomas is here to see you.' 'Send him in.' Peter Thorne replaced the telephone and wondered how best to approach the problem. Frank Thomas peered round the office door, came in and accepted the offer of a chair. He was short and plump, with a round face, brown eyes, brown hair, brown moustache and pale complexion. His uniform was not at its best — both he and it were tired after a long night flight across the Atlantic and he'd been particularly annoyed, on his arrival, to find a note asking him to see the flight manager 'at his earliest convenience'. Now, here he was, bemused and grumpy, wondering what the hell was going on.

'Good trip? Cup of coffee? How d'you like it?'

'Black, please.'

By the look of him, Thorne thought he might need it. He called his secretary for the coffee to be sent in and stayed silent for a while, feeling the need to buy time before broaching the subject. At last he said, 'D'you remember a trip you did in November, London to Teheran?

31

Let me see,' and, consulting, some papers on his desk, 'Wednesday the 30th.'

He watched and waited while Thomas rummaged in his briefcase. Captain Peter Thorne, known behind his back as 'Prickly', could not abide disorder; his desk, like the man himself, was meticulously tidy — files, in-tray, out-tray, blotter and pens, all carefully aligned in neat right-angles.

At last Thomas found his logbook and opened it at the relevant page. 'Yes, that was me. Had a delay out of London, nearly went out of hours. Problem with one of the generators — but they fixed it just in time before the standby crew was called. And it happened again out of Frankfurt, but we didn't exceed the crew duty hours. Is that what you wanted to talk about?'

'No — nothing to do with that.' Thorne opened the file on his desk and pretended to read an official looking letter. After a long pause, he leant forward, rested his elbows on the desk, steepled his fingers and stared at Thomas over his half-moon glasses. 'I think you ought to know there's been one hell of a stink at the Foreign Office. They summoned the Chairman. The Soviets have made a complaint — something about straying into their airspace. A full-blown diplomatic incident, and it looks like your flight. The Chairman is now demanding an explanation and I need to know what happened. What do you say to that, did you notice anything odd?'

'No — only the delays out of London and Frankfurt. Look — here in my logbook — see, I made a short note about the electrics. But that was over three months ago. Don't remember much else except being bloody tired when we got to Teheran. That I do remember.'

'Well, let me tell you what I know. See if it jogs some thoughts. The Russians say they sent up some fighters to intercept you.' Thorne pushed a map across his desk and pointed to a position south of Baku. 'About here, over the Caspian.'

Thomas stood up, looked for somewhere to put down his coffee and leant over the map. 'No one said anything to us. We followed the usual route after Ankara, Sivas, Tatvan, Van, then Tabriz; airways all the way to Teheran. Had to go round a bit of bad weather here, somewhere before Lake Van. That was all.'

Thorne continued to observe him minutely. Despite his dishevelled appearance, Thomas seemed composed with no indication of any concern about suddenly being called to see the flight manager. He decided to come to the point.

'My problem is this. Whatever it was that happened, the proverbial has really hit the fan. Bounced all the way up to Kosygin, back down to Gromyko and then to our ambassador in Moscow. Seems they saw you on radar heading out towards the Caspian Sea and now they are accusing Her Majesty's Government of mounting a spying mission. Of course, our side is saying it's all nonsense, a Soviet plot to embarrass the West, trying to score points at the nuclear talks in Geneva. But the Yanks are blaming us. I'm sure you know how sensitive these things can be.'

Thomas didn't. Neither really did Thorne, all he knew was he'd been on the receiving end of a very irate telephone call from the Chairman. He waited, watching Thomas, wondering whether the gravity of the situation would slowly sink in. Perhaps the pressure of silence would push Thomas to offer the explanation he expected.

'But we never went anywhere near the Caspian, we just followed the airway. Look,' and Thomas traced the route with his finger from Van to Tabriz and down to Teheran. 'I'm sure of that.'

'Well, something happened. They scrambled fighters from an airbase near Baku. The top brass in the Kremlin was informed. Our ambassador in Moscow was carpeted. Accusations of a spying flight. Harold pissed off because the FO hadn't told him. The US embarrassed in Geneva. And now the Chairman's jumping up and down, saying the Foreign Secretary bent his ear something rotten. He's not a happy bunny, and he's demanding explanations. The story's a little muddled, you know what Brown is like. And now it's all landed on my plate!'

'But nothing happened.'

'And there's more — It gets worse. Seems

there's some sort of deadlock in Geneva over on-site inspection requirements. It looks as though Gromyko's using the incident to put a spanner in the works, twist a few arms, gain more concessions, something like that. The Americans are accusing us of buggering it all up.'

Captain Thomas looked steadily back — there really was nothing he could say.

'I've taken the liberty of having our nav people analyse the communications logs.' Thorne carefully moved his in-tray so he could find room to lay the logs out on the desk. 'The superintendent has highlighted this note here, the one saying you made a slight deviation to avoid some weather and — also — that you were fifteen minutes late into Teheran. I think that needs a little more explanation.'

Thomas looked at the proffered logs. There were some jotted calculations querying the extra flight time, but that was all. He really couldn't see a problem, but he did know a thing or two about meteorology, it was a special interest of his. 'I think you'll find the jet stream was a little further north than forecast. Less tail wind — more time,' was all he said.

Thorne, better versed in the peculiarities of human nature than the vagaries of meteorology, was in no mood to be blinded by science. 'You weren't having a catnap, were you?'

Frank Thomas, captain first class, FRMetS,

with over 30 years of flying experience, drew himself up as far as his small stature would allow. He'd served in Coastal Command throughout the war, flown Sunderlands on long patrols out over the Atlantic, had attacked a U-Boat, had won a DFC for a very dicey engagement with a Focke-Wulf Condor, he was not going to accept aspersions of that nature from a pilot who had mainly flown desks. He looked at his flight manager and said very icily, 'When I say nothing unusual happened, I mean nothing unusual happened. Ask the rest of the crew.'

'We already have.'

'And?'

'Said the same as you.'

'Well. There you have it.'

Thorne removed his glasses and returned the steady gaze. He was in a real quandary. On the one hand, he had the whole hierarchy bearing down upon him and, on the other, here was Frank Thomas, someone he'd known a long time, looking disdainfully back at him across his desk.

'If you don't mind, I would like to be getting home. It's been a long night and now I have to drive to the other side of Oxford.' And with that, Thomas returned his logbook to his briefcase, closed it, buttoned his jacket and stood up. 'Is there anything more you want to say, because I really can't think of anything? Normal flight, Russkies inventing problems. And in view of those talks you mentioned, rather convenient, don't you think?'

Bloody flight managers, he grumbled to himself as he left the office, why pick on me? Other airlines were flying that night — could have been any of 'em.

After the door closed, Thorne thought for a while. He had already taken the precaution of having one of his people contact Turkish ATC, but that had drawn a blank — there was no civil radar coverage in that area. He had also rung an old colleague in the Ministry of Defence — but no dice, not even on the QT. MoD was having its own internal difficulties; they certainly did not want to go cap in hand to the Yanks to see if their defence radars had noticed anything. Northern Turkey had been a very sensitive area since the recent Cuban Missile Crisis. Best leave sleeping dogs lie, they told him.

◊◊◊

'Well — what do you think?' Thorne looked across the table at the engineering manager and the navigation superintendent. He had asked them both to join him in his office to discuss the results of their interviews with the other three crew members. He now wanted their individual views.

The engineering manager responded first,

'Angus is a good man, conscientious and reliable. If anything unusual happened, I'm sure he would have told me. I went through his fuel and instrument logs, they're all correct. He also wrote up a detailed analysis of the electrical failure that delayed them in London and Frankfurt. The maintenance engineers were very pleased, said it helped them fix a long-term problem with one of the generators.'

'And the two co-pilots?'

'Ralph Moss was in the right-hand seat—that we do know,' replied the nav superintendent.

'I don't think we need bother too much about the junior one, seems he was dozing at the nav table.

I've said my piece, maybe you should interview him too, tell him to sharpen his ideas up. It's Ralph we need to concentrate on. Everything he says checks with what Thomas has told you, but something doesn't quite add up. Can't put my finger on it. Just doesn't feel right.'

'What d'you mean?'

'Look here.' The nav superintendent spread the airways chart, the flight plan and the comms logs across the table. 'All the times at the reporting points across Europe are close to flight plan. They all agree until passing Ankara. Then they start losing time — substantially. And there's a note here about flying around some weather. Don't know what you think, but the writing looks different, I think something else must have happened too.'

'Thomas thought the jet stream was further north than forecast, would that explain it?'

'Possibly, but unlikely. The forecast could've been wrong, you know how unreliable they are out there. The fuel flight plan was based on a 90-knot tailwind, if that dropped to zero it could account for the extra fifteen minutes. But, of course, we don't know what the actual wind really was. Neither do we know how many extra miles they may have flown dodging the thunderstorms.'

'Were any storms forecast?'

'Not as far as I know. There could have been some, or it could be an invention. It all seems too neat to me. An extra ten miles going round storms would only add a couple of minutes.'

Thorne left the table and stared out of the window. 'I suppose we have three possibilities. One, the Russians have invented it all — but why would they do that? Two, the crew did stray off course and are covering it up. Three, the Russians saw them deviate north around the storms and over-reacted. Any thoughts?'

'There is a fourth,' suggested the nav superintendent, 'I have heard the Russians sometimes broadcast strong signals on the same frequencies as the radio beacons. The RAF have reported some strange anomalies — here, near Lake Van. And back in April '59, an Avro Tudor on a military charter crashed here into Mount Suphan just north of Lake Van. There were rumours it might have been lured off course.'

'I can see why the Russians might want to confuse a military flight, but why would they do that to ours? D'you think there was one there at the same time?'

'I've checked, but MoD say no.'

'They would, wouldn't they.'

'As I see it,' chipped in the engineering manager, 'There's no proof either way. Captain Thomas and his crew seem to have a cast iron story. We'll never get anything out of the Russians. The Yanks are unlikely to reveal what they know given the sensitivity along the border. And the Turks are in their pocket.'

The nav superintendent agreed. 'I don't think we're going to resolve this one, I have my doubts — we all do, there's something very fishy about it. I'm sure the crew are covering something up.'

'I think you're right. But how do I explain it to the Chairman?'

'Would you like me to draft a memo?'

'No. I'll brief him verbally, leave him some wiggle room when he talks to the Foreign Office. George Brown can be rather unpredictable — "tired and emotional" I think is the expression.'

The meeting over, Thorne rose from the table and again gazed out of the window. He was a tall man, slim with beady eyes, greying hair and a sharp nose. For a long time, he stood motionless like a heron intent on a fish. On the tarmac outside, some men were working on an aircraft, the engine cowlings open, revealing the mass of pipes beneath. He felt a much greater affinity with those convoluted pipes than with the politics of his current conundrum.

Most probably, he thought, the crew had

made a cock-up and did not want to admit it. He knew about Frank Thomas's reputation — no proof, just rumours about sleeping on the job. He wasn't called 'Dormouse Toormouse' for nothing. But what should he tell the Chairman? He could stick by his crew in what was probably a lie, or he could admit the navigation error. Were the Russians inventing the incident to score points in Geneva? Had they used strong broadcast stations to interfere with the navigational radio beacons? There were certainly rumours they'd done so in the past. And did they, or the Americans, have any radar records to prove the aircraft had strayed into Soviet airspace? That was the important point. But what was best for the company? What would be the easiest course for the Chairman? There were times when 'less said, soonest mended' was the best motto. He returned to his desk and picked up the phone, he needed an ally.

His immediate boss, the flight operations director, was in and could see him straightaway. Together they decided the easiest way out was to explain to the Chairman that there had been no navigational error, the flight had never entered Soviet airspace, it had only made a very small deviation around a thunderstorm. They thought the Russians had probably seen this on radar and. thinking the aircraft was about to enter Soviet airspace, had overreacted. Now they were blowing it up out of all proportion — let the Foreign Office decide why that might be. They were confident the Chairman could explain all this to George Brown, secure in the knowledge that their thorough investigation had shown the flight to be entirely normal — they had the documentary evidence to prove it.

But Thorne knew in his heart how thin the evidence really was and that the thunderstorms were almost certainly non-existent. He was not entirely happy being party to what he was fairly sure was a cover-up.

◊◊◊

Come April, Ralph Moss was amazed he'd got away with it, there'd been no comeback since the uncomfortable interview with the navigation superintendent — no phone calls, no peremptory notes requiring his presence again in the office. What had started as a minor error, and which he thought he had skilfully hidden, had suddenly blown up into an international incident and then had gone away. Why?

They had certainly been tired after the delays in London and Frankfurt. He also knew about old Dormouse's reputation, it was common knowledge in the fleet, so he had not been surprised when the captain said he needed a catnap as they passed Zagreb in the night — he and Angus could easily mind the shop while the captain slumbered and the young lad minded his own business at the nav table. And all had gone swimmingly until after Ankara when, in the quiet of the cockpit, he had begun to nod off too.

He remembered his surprise at being suddenly woken by ATC calling urgently on the radio asking why they had the missed the last two position reports. He remembered even more clearly being horrified by the sight of moonlight glinting on water ahead. He still had nightmares about that many months later. And he certainly remembered that cold chill down his spine when he checked the radar and recognised the unmistakeable shape of the coastline around Baku. It could only be the Caspian and that meant they must be somewhere over Azerbaijan, in Soviet territory well north of the Iranian border. He had turned swiftly south, thanking God they were still over land, and feeling an intense relief as he saw the navigation needles swing towards Tabriz. With luck, they would soon be in Iranian airspace.

The captain had slept on. Angus hadn't noticed, he'd been busy writing a long engineering report about the electrical problems, and the lad remained dozing at the nav table — only Ralph knew how close they had come to an almighty cock-up. But what next? Fortunately, Iranian ATC had not queried their next position reports. Nearing top of descent, he had woken the captain, giving him the new ETA, saying they'd had to fly around a few thunderstorms and the tail wind must have dropped.

The captain said something about jet stream forecasts being unreliable. That was all.

After landing, Ralph had gathered up all the comms logs, found a blank sheet, made some quick calculations, added a few extra minutes to each leg after passing Ankara to account for the extra fifteen minutes, substituted the doctored page for the original and then carefully filed it with all the paperwork and logs in the voyage report envelope. He was pretty sure his carefully crafted times would stand up to scrutiny, he even made a brief note about avoiding some fictitious storms to further muddy the waters.

Now, five months later, he was the only

one who really knew what had happened. But Thorne, despite having convinced the Chairman there had been no navigational error, remained troubled by his complicity in what he knew to be a convenient deceit. It would be difficult now to take any action against the crew — he had no proof, only a very strong suspicion. Ralph might have got away with it for now, but he would forever be a marked man.

The Test Flight

Seven men and a gleaming aircraft. The 747 is waiting on the tarmac after a major overhaul, during which it had been almost completely taken apart and put back together again. Its new paintwork and polished wings dazzle in the morning sun. Seven men in the chief engineer's office pore over books, charts, graphs and schedules, preparing themselves for the coming flight. Five are crew, two are engineers who have worked hard to have the aircraft ready in time. Precision is the order of the day. Precise preparation and precise flying. Each must know his task.

Garry Webber is an avionics engineer. He knows the radio and computer systems inside out. Dusty Miller is similarly qualified on the hydraulic systems. Both men are licensed maintenance engineers who understand intimately the insides of this complex machine. They are on the flight, partly as a reward for their hard work during the overhaul, but also, because they can offer advice should anything go wrong.

THE TEST FLIGHT

Al Dowland is 'working the panel'. He will be sitting at the flight engineer's station, checking the systems. Before he went flying, he too had been a ground engineer and knows them every bit as well as Garry and Dusty. Don Green, the other flight engineer, is ex-Navy. He will be acting as observer, recording the many checks and instrument readings during the flight. The two co-pilots are also men of long experience. Tom Perrin will be in the right hand seat, while Pete Martin will be on the jump seat acting as 'master of ceremonies'. I am Ray Longford, the air test qualified captain, ex-RAF, with over twenty years of airline flying under my belt. All five of us will be working hard during this four-hour flight.

Clear flying conditions are essential — no turbulence and a good visible horizon. Together, we examine the met forecast and decide that out over the North Sea, east of Norfolk, is the best option. We take time to make sure everyone knows the exact sequence of manoeuvres and tests. I discuss with Pete, who will be recording the data at each of the 'test points'— climb performance, stall speeds, max speed warnings and timing things like raising and lowering flaps and landing gear — the way we will coordinate each item, so everything is noted down correctly. He has been on many air tests before and knows exactly what to do. Tom, however, is a little concerned about the stalls. Although he has many years of flying experience, he is new to this kind of flying, so I suggest he stays behind for a moment while the others go out to prepare the aircraft.

'Even though this is not a normal airline flight,' I tell him, 'it's definitely not experimental test flying, it's more in the nature of a check flight. See everything works as advertised. But I won't deny there isn't some additional risk.'

Before joining the 747 fleet, Tom had flown BAC One-Elevens, a very successful small T-tailed twin jet airliner. It had sold well and was a good aeroplane. But one had been lost on an early test flight back in 1963 when it became locked in a deep stall, crashing into a field in Wiltshire, killing all on board. 'That was always in the back of our minds,' he explained.

'Yes, I can understand that, but the 747 is amazingly docile. The stall characteristics are benign. However, there's always the slight possibility of something untoward — a sudden unusual attitude for example — that's why we need a good visible horizon to make it easier to regain control. I've done these tests many times before — it's perfectly straightforward if you know what you're doing.'

I then describe in detail the technique we will use. We will calculate the stall speed for each configuration and for each one I will reduce speed very carefully and very slowly, keeping the wings level with no sideslip. Pete will note the onset of the aerodynamic buffet

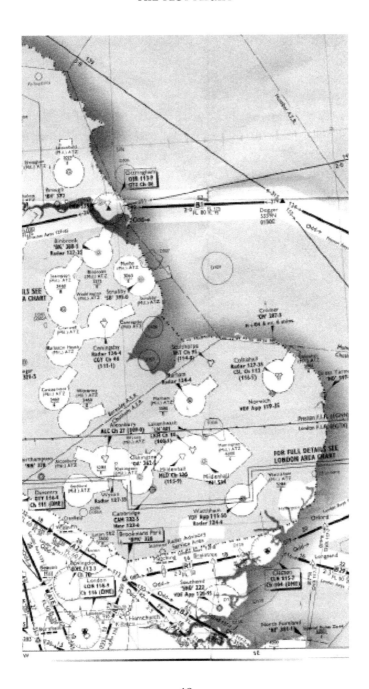

and record the speeds when the stick shaker operates and the moment of the stall itself — when the nose drops. I then describe the clean stall which is unique. The 747 has never been stalled clean. The aerodynamic buffet, which starts early, builds up to such a severe up and down bouncing oscillation that the Boeing test pilots never went to the full stall. Instead, they defined the stall as the maximum acceptable buffet and calibrated the stick shaker to start at that speed.

'It may feel alarming,' I tell Tom, 'and you will need to have your straps really tight, but don't worry, the stick shaker starts well before the buffet becomes too strong.'

I then go on to tell him about another little quirk. Unlike other aircraft, the 747 does not want to pitch nose down as the speed reduces, instead, it remains neutrally stable and just keeps 'motoring on' as the incidence increases. When Dai Davies, the ARB test pilot, flew it he required a little device called a stick nudger to be fitted. It pushes the control column gently forward when the stick shaker starts and this restores normal longitudinal stability.

'Neat idea isn't it. All the other stalls, with the flaps down are normal and much more gentle. We'll do 'em all at 15,000ft to give us plenty of room — very occasionally a wing drops and then we need to lose around 3,000ft before climbing back up again for the next one.'

'The rest of the flight is very straight forward,' I add, and I go on to explain some of the other tests — performance climbs on three and two engines; climbing to 30,000ft to check the pressurisation system; depressurising the cabin to make sure the cabin altitude warnings work, and all the passenger oxygen masks drop out.

'We'll be on oxygen for that one. Then we have some peace and quiet on autopilot while the engineers check cruise figures and a whole lot of other things on their panel. After that, we dive to the maximum permitted Mach number — the 747's handling qualities are really good at high speed, no problem at all, very controllable, no Mach tuck like the 707. D'you know, it's the only aircraft I've ever flown which has no handling vices at all. After all of that, we shut down engines to check we can restart them, and then fly home. On the way back, we check the alternate systems for lowering the flaps and landing gear — that takes a long time — and while we do that, you'll be busy coordinating our return into controlled airspace with ATC and the clearance back to Gatwick.

'Your most important job in all of this is to keep a good look out for other aircraft, to watch the navigation and keep a common-sense eye on everything — if you don't like something, sing out and we'll discuss it — you are 'long stop'!'

When Tom is satisfied, I phone ATC to discuss the flight plan and explain the manoeuvres we will be doing. Then, together, we walk out to the aircraft.

'What a gorgeous day to go flying,' I remark as we leave the gloom of the hangar. 'These flights are always fun — real hand flying for a change, very little autopilot stuff. Much better than the normal bus driving!' Tom looks a little sideways, I'm not sure he entirely believes me.

I wish good morning to the group of engineers gathered around the bottom of the steps and we climb aboard. Up on the flight deck, the others are already checking the flight control hydraulic power shut-off switches. Why we have to do this, I will never know, but it's on the Civil Aviation Authority's Flight Test Schedule, so we do it. It's also hard work, that's why I leave it to the young blokes like Pete. He is in my seat pumping away at the rudder pedals as each switch is selected to off to make sure the hydraulic power really has been shut off — upper and lower rudders, left and right outboard ailerons in turn. I suggest

THE TEST FLIGHT

Tom climbs into the right-hand seat and starts on the normal pre-flight checks. 'Just be super critical and record anything that isn't absolutely right.'

Al hands me the Tech Log, the maintenance history of the aircraft, which of course is clean after a major overhaul. I sign it and check the fuel load is correct — we need to have the centre of gravity position just right — neither too far forward, nor too far aft.

Pete finishes his hard work on the rudder pedals. 'She's all yours, boss,' he puffs, as he climbs out of the left-hand seat. I jump in and check my instrument panel and set the navigation systems up for our departure route out of Gatwick to Brookmans Park, a radio beacon some 20 miles north of London up the M1. From there, we will leave controlled airspace and fly northeast under Eastern Radar, a military radar unit.

Our initial checks complete, we start on all the extra ones required in the test schedule — the take-off configuration warning horn (in normal operation, it makes a loud insistent beeping noise if the flaps, trim and other essential items are not set correctly for take-off); the functioning of the trim system, which controls the position of the large horizontal stabiliser in the tail; the flap safety switches, which isolate the flaps from hydraulic power; the stick shaker, which gives warning of an impending stall; the emergency lights; the standby electrical power; the emergency

53

intercom and many other systems such as the transfer switches on the pilots instrument panels. All the radio and instrument systems are duplicated, normally the number one systems provide inputs to the captain's panel and the number two to the co-pilot's side — operating these switches allows the captain to receive inputs from the number two systems and vice versa.

At last, when we are ready, we start the engines and complete yet another set of checks. Tom calls ATC, 'Gatwick ground, Gryphon Tango Zulu, ready for taxi from the BNAA maintenance area.' Our 747 has British North Atlantic Airlines' glorious Golden Gryphon emblazoned on its tail, Tango Zulu are the last two letters of the aircraft's registration — hence our call sign.

We are cleared to runway 26, make a normal take-off and follow the standard instrument departure route towards Brookmans Park, climbing to 6,000 feet which suits us well, as the first set of tests will be slam acceleration checks on each engine and these have to be carried out below 7,000 feet. Tom contacts Eastern Radar as we leave controlled airspace and informs them that we will be slowing to 160 knots and remaining at 6,000 feet while we do these. 'Tell 'em we can accept any heading, but it's important to keep at this speed and altitude,' I say to Tom.

When I am ready, Al leans forward and pushes the number one thrust lever forward to the correct go-around power and marks its position on the quadrant with a chinagraph pencil. He then pulls it back to idle power and waits for the engine to stabilise. He records the N_1 and N_2 — the speeds of the two turbine spools. 'Ready boss?' When I say I am, he slams the thrust lever forward to the marked position and notes the time taken for the engine to accelerate. He does this for each engine in turn while I keep the aircraft straight and maintain 160 knots with the other three engines. It's a bit of a juggling act using power, rudder and aileron controls. 'That all checks OK,' Don says, and we go on to the next item on the list — the first of the performance climbs.

'Tell Radar our next test will be a performance climb,' I say to Tom. 'We can accept any heading they want, but we must have a straight run. Ask them for 30 miles and a block of altitude between flight level 60 and 120.' Tom negotiates this, while Don checks the aircraft's weight and consults the graphs to work out the engine power settings required, and I put the number 4 engine to idle ready for the test.

Pete reads out the requirements. 'All anti-icing off, three air conditioning packs on, gear up, flaps at 10,' he says, 'then go-around power on one, two and three. The V_2 speed is 149 knots. I'll record the altitude every 30 seconds; Don will record the outside temperatures and engine readings every minute. Tell me when you're ready, Ray, and I'll start the stopwatch.'

'Radar says you are good for the climb on a heading of 080 degrees and they've blocked off the altitudes we need,' Tom advises.

I turn onto 080 and ask Al to set go-around power on the three good engines. I trim the aircraft and settle it in a climb at 149 knots — V_2 is the speed to climb out after take-off should there be a real engine failure. 'OK — go,' I say and concentrate on climbing at exactly this speed for the next five minutes. Silence reigns as each of us remains fixed upon his appointed task.

After two minutes, Pete says, 'I've recorded the trim settings, what does your ASI read and what's yours, Tom?' We both say 149 knots. Then he turns to Don and Al, 'Have you noted all the engine readings?' I continue the climb — it's important not to deviate by more than a knot.

'Time's up,' says Pete, 'What's the aircraft weight?

We have climbed to just over flight level 110, I bring the power up on number four, ask Tom to bring in the flaps while I ease back the other three engines and continue the climb to flight level 120 where I level off.

'Tom, tell Radar we can now accept any heading and need a further climb to flight level 150 while we test the fuel dumping system.'

Don confirms the three-engine climb met all the specifications. Tom says we have permission to dump, Al prepares the fuel panel for dumping and Don goes downstairs into the cabin. He will coordinate with Al on the interphone as he looks out of the cabin windows to confirm when the fuel starts and stops pouring from the dump pipes out on the wing. I leave them to it and turn onto the new heading Radar has requested and continue the climb to flight level 150.

It is quiet for a moment while Al and Don complete the fuel dump test. Pete advises the next performance climb is on two engines, we can start at the current altitude. I work out in my head the distance and altitudes we will need and ask Tom to tell Radar we require a straight run for ten minutes and to block off 60 miles on any heading they wish between flight level 120 and 180. From long experience, I know the aircraft may either climb or descend — it all depends on the outside air temperature. It's better to ask for a generous amount of airspace now rather than negotiate a change later, part way through the test, and then have to do it all over again.

While Tom talks to the radar controller, Al, Don and Pete check the weight and ready themselves for the next set of test recordings. Radar advises they cannot give us a straight run at the moment but, if we stay on 080 for another 30 miles, they will be able to turn us onto a heading of 330 degrees for the run at our requested altitudes. I say that's OK, and we await further instructions.

When they turn us onto the new heading,

I put numbers 1 and 2 engines to idle and Al sets 3 and 4 to max continuous power. I trim out the rudder loads, needing nearly full right rudder, and settle on the required speed — 234 knots exactly. Pete and Don perform the same tasks as before — altitude readings every 30 seconds and temperature readings every minute.

Al adjusts the power as needed, 'Do you know the one about ...?' And he cracks a dirty joke to see if he can break my concentration. I laugh and tell him to stop pissing me about, but I have to work to contain a small deviation of airspeed. We are old friends and he usually tries this on at some stage. We climb steadily on until our time is up and level out at flight level 165. I restore all the engines to a normal power setting and wind out the rudder trim.

Next come the stalls. We are already near the correct altitude, and I can see The Wash out to my left and the Humber estuary further north. I talk to the controller myself, 'Eastern Radar, Gryphon Tango Zulu, our next tests are the stalls, can you block off the area immediately around us and down to flight level 100, the height loss can sometimes be unpredictable?'

'Roger Tango Zulu, I'll have to turn you south before you start. Airway Blue One is twenty miles north of you and there's a military exercise to your west. Give me a few minutes while I coordinate.'

I acknowledge and wait for him to call us

back. Meanwhile, I prepare the crew. We secure all loose objects while Don and Pete check the aircraft's weight and work out the speeds — trim speed 218 knots, stick shake 187. Everyone straps in tight, including the two ground engineers in the upper deck cabin aft of the flight deck. On this one, the buffet can be quite violent.

'Gryphon Tango Zulu, I have your clearance. Turn now onto heading 170 and descend to flight level 150. You are cleared for your exercise, not below flight level 100.' Tom reads back the instructions and I reduce the power on all four engines to idle, letting the speed decay slowly. When we reach 218 knots, exactly 1.3 times the stall speed, I stop trimming and continue reducing speed at one knot per second. The aerodynamic buffet begins and builds in intensity as the air flow starts to break away from the wings. 200 knots, 190, then at 185 knots the stick shaker rattles, the nudger nudges, and I lower the nose to regain speed.

'Within limits,' Pete shouts above the din, 'only two knots slow.'

'Well, that wasn't too bad, was it?' I say to Tom as we climb back to flight level 150. 'Now for the flap 1 stall.' Pete times the flaps as Tom extends them, 5 seconds for the trailing edge flaps, 10 seconds for the leading-edge ones, and we ready ourselves for the next stall.

'Trim 176, shake 166,' advises Pete. Again, we go through the same procedure; the buffet is less, and the stick shaker operates at the correct speed. We lose about 1,000 feet in a shallow dive as we regain airspeed and then I climb back to flight level 150. Air beneath is valuable in these exercises — there's an old piloting adage about useless things in aviation — runway behind, air above and fuel in the bowser!

For the flap 10 stall, we again time the flaps as they run out, it takes 40 seconds, and all the times are correct. I ready myself for the full stall. Pete extracts the speeds from the graph — trim 156, stick shake 133, stall 117. Again, I reduce speed at 1 knot per second, the stick shaker starts its rattle right on schedule and continues until the nose drops at 117 knots. Abruptly, we are pointing nose down towards the earth, I gently advance the power and let the speed build before easing back on the controls — too much and we will be in a secondary stall, so I let the aircraft descend some 2,000 feet before climbing back to flight level 150. Pete confirms the speeds were all correct and we prepare for the full stall in the landing configuration — landing gear down and flap 30. We note the time they take to run out.

So far so good, I think to myself, everything has been immaculate — good weather, good teamwork, and every test exactly according to the book figures.

'OK everyone, this will be the last one. What are the speeds, Pete?'

'Trim 141, shake 114, stall 105,' he says. 'And during the recovery you'll need to use power to increase speed to check the flap load relief, it should come in between 169 and 176 knots. But do not exceed 180 with flaps still at 30.'

This system automatically brings the flaps in from 30 to 25 degrees so as not to overload them. The flaps are a complicated structure, like little wings that run out on tracks on the trailing edge of the wing to provide more lift for landing and take-off. Flap 30 is the maximum extension used only for landing.

I ease the thrust levers back to idle power and start to reduce speed. I stop trimming at 141 knots and count to myself, 130, 120, 114 — there's the stick shaker right on schedule; keep pulling back on the controls — nearly there, 110, 108, 105, controls fully back now — and the nose drops. Keep pointing it down, ease on some power, speed building, 120, 130, 140, 150, 160, 170, then — THUMP! An ominous distant thump and a sudden lurch to starboard. I have to apply nearly full left aileron and a hard push on the rudder to contain the roll and yaw. The aircraft vibrates in a way I've never known before.

'Don't touch anything,' I shout, 'It's still controllable. Whatever you do, don't move the flaps or the gear.'

'Flap asymmetry, they've locked out,' calls Tom, pointing to the flap position indicators on the centre panel. 'The needles are split.

They've stopped halfway between 25 and 30.'

'Ray,' Al shouts to me, 'I suggest we put both trailing edge flap arm switches to 'Arm' right now. I'll start the drill while Don goes back to look out of the windows.'

'Good idea,' I reply, 'But don't do anything that moves the flaps or gear. We need to assess the damage first.' I steady the aircraft at its current altitude and maintain a speed of 150 knots. Then I trim out the rudder loads and keep applying aileron — I have to keep the control wheel tilted far over to the left, nearly 90 degrees from normal. 'Tom, don't declare an emergency yet, but tell Radar we have a problem and need to maintain this altitude and heading while we assess it.'

Al completes the relevant parts of the check list, and we await Don's report. 'At least it's still flyable,' I observe, mainly to reassure Tom. 'And we're already in the landing configuration — that's a bonus.'

Don returns with a very worried Dusty close behind. 'Ray,' he says, 'the inboard flaps on the starboard side are twisted out of kilter, the inboard ends look OK, but the outboard end is cocked up and some parts are missing. It's hard to tell, but the good thing is the spoilers still look OK.'

Dusty chips in, 'Captain, I think the out-board flap track's broken, United had one go at San Francisco a couple of years back, the spoiler support beam was damaged too. It happened late on the approach. But they landed OK. We'd better watch the number four hydraulic system — it powers the inboard spoilers.'

By this time, I have the aircraft under easier control — apart from the vibration and needing to hold the control wheel hard over to the left. I turn to Tom, 'I've trimmed the rudder, all you have to do is keep straight and level and maintain 150 knots, I'd like to hand over control in a moment while we have a think. You ready?' He says he is. 'OK, you have control.'

'I have control,' comes the response, and I turn to the others.

'The aircraft is flyable, we're already in the landing configuration which helps if we have to make an emergency landing and we've isolated the flaps so they can't be moved. It's not an emergency yet, but we do need to tell ATC. Pete, can you call company and advise them of our problem. Al, Don and Dusty, you three put your heads together and see if you can think of anything more. And while you all do that I'll talk to ATC, the sooner we're back on the ground the better — before something drops off.' I am acutely aware that we are out over the sea and it may be half an hour before we can land — will the flaps stay attached that long?

'My R/T,' and I call ATC. 'Pan, Pan, Pan, Eastern Radar, Gryphon Tango Zulu, we have a problem with our flaps.'

Eastern Radar replies immediately, 'Roger

63

your Pan, Tango Zulu, what assistance do you need?'

'During the last stall, our right inboard flaps failed, they're badly damaged but the aircraft is still under control. I may have limited manoeuvrability, so I want to remain on this heading, speed and altitude while we assess the problem.'

'Roger, do you need an immediate landing?'

'We may do, but not yet. I don't think it's advisable to fly back to Gatwick past London in case something drops off. Would you ask Bedford if they can accept us?' Eastern Radar acknowledges and says he will talk to Bedford. I know Bedford well, it has a long runway which is wider than normal, something that might be very useful.

While Tom flies the aircraft, the rest of us review the situation. We all agree a diversion to Bedford seems the best option. The immediate drill for the flap lockout has been completed. We agree it's best to leave the flaps and gear where they are. All the hydraulic systems are serviceable — for now — but we need to be prepared to lose number four. I ask Al to read the top of descent check list and we agree to use the 25 flap reference speed (Vref) for the landing.

'Gryphon Tango Zulu, Eastern Radar.' I tell him to go ahead. 'Bedford are willing to accept you but they'd rather you go to Gatwick as they're doing some autoland trials at the moment. What are your intentions?'

'We'll discuss with company and come back to you. Meanwhile, I'd like to turn onto a heading of around 210 so we're nearer some suitable airfields, I'm worried about these flaps. We have good control at the moment but I can't be certain of that if we lose some flap sections ... and I'd like to descend to flight level 100 and maintain 150 knots.'

'Tango Zulu, turn onto 210 and descend now to flight level 100.'

I acknowledge and turn to Pete who has been talking to company. Their advice is to go to Bedford.

'Ray, the number four hydraulic system's gone — no pressure, no fluid — all gone!'

'That decides it. I have control. Tom, declare a Mayday and say it has to be Bedford. Al, let's have the loss of hydraulic system check list for number four.'

Al switches off the air driven pump and the engine driven pump and reads out the list of affected services. Fortunately, with the flaps already out and the landing gear down, there is nothing significant to do other than selecting the wheel brakes to hydraulic system number one. 'We'll need to watch system one, if we lose that too we'll have no steering and we'll have to select the reserve source for the brakes — that comes from the number two system.'

'Gryphon Tango Zulu, Eastern Radar, we've notified Bedford of your Mayday, their runway in use is 27, the ILS is serviceable, and the weather good, are you ready to copy?'

Tom replies and notes down the weather — wind 230 at 10 knots, CAVOK (which means no cloud and excellent visibility). At least that's another problem out of the way.

'Ask Eastern how many miles to touchdown, I'd like a long straight in approach.'

Tom does so and Eastern confirms we have 60 miles to go and would it be possible to turn right onto heading 250 and descend to flight level 50 to avoid Marham?

I agree and turn very gently. We're now descending through flight level 90, still at 150 knots.

Suddenly the aircraft lurches and the vibration increases. 'Sounds like something's dropped off.

Someone go back and look.'

Don returns. 'Doesn't look good. The fore flap has gone, the number eight spoiler section is bent up and the inner aileron has a corner damaged at the trailing edge. How do the controls feel?'

I try a few exploratory movements — the aircraft responds well, but I have to hold the control wheel even further to the left. I take care to make small inputs, I don't want to do any more damage.

Eastern Radar tells us to turn onto heading 230 which will take us towards Bedford. I comply. We are now passing flight level 60 with 30 miles to run. I am seriously concerned as to what might happen if the whole flap section drops off. Not only could that cause a hard roll to starboard which might be uncontrollable, but bits might also hit the horizontal stabiliser in the tail with unknown consequences. If I can't control it in pitch, we might not be able to land. I don't say anything to the others — they have enough to worry about.

I level out at flight level 50, 'Let's get the approach check out of the way.'

Al reads the checklist and tells me the weight is 231 tonnes, 'Vref for flap 25 is 141 knots.'

I say, 'The landing briefing is very simple. We're already in the landing configuration. Most of the flaps are at 30, the inboards we don't quite know, so I'll use the flap 25 Vref but maintain 150 knots to the threshold. Runway 27 is over 10,000 feet long; threshold elevation is 273 feet. I'll make a visual approach, using the ILS. We'll use auto-brakes, auto-spoilers and reverse thrust — But — there'll be no go-around — we can't risk anything more falling off. Any questions?'

'Gryphon Tango Zulu, Eastern Radar — you're now 15 miles from the field, it should be in your two o'clock. Descend now to 3,000ft, QNH 1008 and turn onto heading 240 — this will bring you towards the ILS centre line. Do you have the field in sight?'

Tom says yes, we do.

'Roger, radar service terminated. Change now to Bedford Tower, frequency 130.0 and good luck.'

Tom thanks them and calls Bedford Tower.

He asks for the ILS frequency as we don't have a chart for the field.

'Gryphon Tango Zulu, Bedford Tower, we have your Mayday, the ILS frequency is 108.3, you are cleared to land runway 27, the wind is 230 at 15 knots, the ceiling and visibility OK, QFE 999. You're number one to land, continue on that heading and call established. Descend at your discretion.'

Tom acknowledges these instructions and I continue down to 3,000 feet. We line up and start a shallow descent towards the runway.

'Tango Zulu, Tower — how many souls on board and what is the state of your flaps?'

'Seven souls on board — flaps are normal except for the starboard inners which are hanging on....... just,' says Tom.

I go on the radio, 'The starboard inners are badly damaged; we think a flap track's broken. We also have a hydraulic system U/S, but expect to make a normal landing. However, we may drop pieces on the runway during the landing roll. At the moment I don't expect any control problems.'

Famous last words, I mutter to myself under my breath.

The vibration continues. It seems to be worse — or is it my imagination? Passing 1,000 feet, I ask Pete to slowly wind out the rudder trim. As he does so, I take the load on the left rudder pedal to keep the aircraft straight. I am now flying with nearly full rudder deflection and the control wheel hard over to the left. I am having difficulty keeping the aircraft pointed towards the runway. It's also one hell of a physical strain, I'll be damn glad when it's over.

We come over the threshold and descend through 30 feet. Ground effect rolls the aircraft to the right. I am only just able to hold it. Despite full left aileron, I land heavily, skidding towards the runway edge. Somehow I manage to straighten up. It wasn't elegant but we're down. The spoilers activate, I apply reverse thrust. We stay on the runway and start slowing down.

'Tango Zulu, we see sparks and fire on your right side. The fire services are standing by.'

'Roger that,' says Tom.

We come to a stop on the runway. Dusty comes bounding onto the flight deck, 'The whole section is trailing along the ground, it came off when we landed, I was watching from the cabin.'

'Any signs of fire?' I ask.

'No. Ruddy great shower of sparks but no fire.'

'Tower, Tango Zulu, we'll hold our position here. We think part of the flaps have broken off — sparks, but no fire. Please ask the fire services to inspect and advise.'

We sit and wait. 'Leave the flaps and spoilers where they are, I don't want anything more graunched! Let's see what the fire chief says, but be ready to evacuate if necessary.'

The Tower comes over the R/T and advises

there is no fire but the inboard flaps are hanging on by their inner ends only, with the outer end trailing on the tarmac. 'Are you able to taxy?'

'Stand by.' I ask Don and Dusty to go down through the electrics bay and out by the hatch behind the nosewheel. 'Take a good look and let me know what you think. I'd like to taxy clear of the runway if at all possible.'

When they return, they explain the outer flap track has broken completely and is scraping on the ground, the fore flap has fallen off, the spoiler support beam is damaged, the inboard aileron has a corner knocked off, and hydraulic fluid is dripping from a broken pipe.

'I'd hold position if I were you,' says Don.

'We'd like to shut down here and inspect the damage,' I tell ATC. 'And thanks for your help — we needed it!'

'That's about the hairiest bloody landing I've ever experienced,' mutters Don.

'It was a bit of a thumper,' I admit.

'I'd give it a nine,' volunteers Pete from behind my seat.

'Yeaah,' drawls Al in his best faux Texan voice. '... On the Richter scale!'

A Strange Request

D'ya remember Geoff Dawkins?' 'Not really.' And I continued filling my cup. Two pilots and a flight engineer were gathered round the coffee machine. The one holding *Speedbird News*, our in-house weekly paper says, 'according to the *Friday Fire Lighter*, in the obits, "Geoffrey Oscar Dawkins, died first of April 1984, funeral to be held next Tuesday at Holy Trinity, Sunningdale."'

The other, 'Couldn't make it up if you tried. God dying on April Fool's Day!'

'Wonder if they'll bury him in his kid gloves,' added Lloyd, the engineer. He was a large man with practical hands, curly blond hair and an amiable smile. Also, a good judge of character. 'Ever fly with the old bastard?'

'No, when he was on 'Seven Ohs', I was on 'Tens'.

'Heard of him?'

'Of course, who hasn't?' Taking my coffee through to my office, I leave them to it.

Some people are blessed with parents possessing little imagination. This was certainly the case for Geoff Dawkins. How he coped at school, I'll never know. When I came across him back in the '60s — well let's just say he'd acquired a certain reputation. He was one of the old 'Atlantic Barons', having flown Stratocruisers, 707s and several other types after leaving RAF Costal Command where he had flown Liberators on anti-submarine patrols during the war. When a colleague pointed him out to me in a hotel bar, I was still a young co-pilot on VC10s. 'A real tarter,' he warned, 'Everything has to be just so. Have to call him 'Sir' — all the time. Flies in kid gloves. Behind his back, they call him God. Sometimes I think he thinks he is.'

Over the years, I never saw him again, only heard the odd rumours about his lofty demeanour and his love of golf. 'Goff,' he called it, and everyone laughed.

A few months after the conversation round the coffee machine, Barry Fellows, a pilot now retired, phoned asking if he could come to see me. He had a strange request and hoped I could help. By then, I was a manager on the 747 fleet, we were in the middle of a very busy period, but I could fit him in the following day. I wondered what his strange request might be.

When he arrived, he was somewhat diffident in his approach. 'I don't quite know how to begin. Did you ever know Geoff Dawkins? He died recently, lived not far from me near Sunningdale, used to see him occasionally. On the golf course. Didn't know him really, but my wife saw quite a lot of his wife, er, well … widow now.'

He stopped. I waited.

'She asked my wife to ask me.' A longer pause. 'To arrange for his ashes to be scattered at 30 West. Said it was his dying wish.'

'Have you tried a shipping company? Or the Navy, or the RAF?'

'No, I don't know anyone in the services. Can't approach a shipping company — not officially. They wouldn't be interested, probably against the law. I thought you might be able to help … or know someone who could.'

I didn't. I've been asked many strange things in my life but never anything like this. Much as I'd like to help, I told him, I really couldn't see how I could do anything. He said he was very sorry to have bothered me and left.

◊◊◊

I enjoy conundrums, especially those that are unusual — as this one most certainly was. But, why 30^0 West? What was so special for Geoff Dawkins about this line of longitude halfway across the North Atlantic? I knew in the old days, on Strats, when piston engines were so unreliable, aircrews felt a huge sense of relief having reached this midpoint — it was all 'downhill' the rest of the way, but it had to be more than that. Was his wife an old battle-axe, and here he'd felt he'd escaped the apron strings? Or quite the reverse, he was looking forward to a welcome home? Did he have a mistress in New York, or had he met his wife in mid-Atlantic? Stranger things have happened on aircraft.

For several nights, as I lay in bed, I thought again about Barry's strange request. It intrigued me. I knew there had to be a solution. But dropping something from a civil airliner was next to impossible and almost certainly illegal. I couldn't just open a door or window and throw him out. You'd need to depressurise the whole aircraft to do that. Did I know any RAF Nimrod pilots who could help? They flew long, over-water patrols and dropped flares and things into the sea. But did they ever go out over the Atlantic as far as 30⁰ West and, if they did, who could I approach? These ideas rattled around my brain for a while until I suddenly remembered the hoary old story about the flight engineer who had hooked up a vacuum cleaner hose to the sextant mount. He'd used the suction through the hole to clean the flight deck. But that had been a long time ago on a VC10, and — so the story went — halfway through the process, the hose had sucked itself out through the hole and had flapped around on the outside of the fuselage until it broke free. A great joke, but perhaps I had better explain.

A STRANGE REQUEST

Up at 35,000 feet, the air is thin, so the cabin needs to be pressurised in order to maintain a comfortable cabin altitude for the passengers. The flight engineer's party trick involved using the sextant mount in the flight deck ceiling as a vacuum cleaner. The pressure difference between the inside and the outside of the aircraft was more than enough to suck the dust in the flight deck out through the hose.

Back in the days before inertial navigation systems (INS), when navigators used periscopic sextants for astro-navigation, this mount allowed the navigator to pass the periscopic end of the sextant through to the outside of the aircraft so that he could see the stars. There was an elaborate system of locking lugs, levers and shutters to seal the hole when the sextant was not in use. And believe it or not, the Boeing 747 was equipped with just such a mount even though it had never been used

for navigation since the aircraft systems had been designed around three INSs — inertial navigation systems.

Here was the solution to my problem.

The next day, I decided to take a peek in one of the 747s in the hangar. I waited until the lunch hour when few engineers were about and went to examine the sextant mount. Yes, there it was — exactly the same as the ones I had used on VC10s. It took me only a few minutes to check how to hold back the locking lugs and to operate the lever which opened the shutter in the hole. I figured that, if the flight engineer could insert a vacuum hose so easily, I could do the same with a short piece of pipe. That evening, I found a piece of copper water pipe in my garage. I rounded the end slightly so it would fit more easily into the mount and made a second visit to the hangars to test my theory. Once my preparations were in place, I phoned Barry with the good news.

A few days later, he arrived in my office holding a large paper parcel which concealed the urn containing the ashes. 'Sorry it's like this,' he said, 'Didn't want people to see. Bit embarrassing wandering round here carrying an urn.'

I agreed. It would be even more so, taking it onto an aircraft full of passengers. It was rather large. How on earth was I going to hide it in my pilot's briefcase? And what would customs say when I arrived in the US with an empty urn? Over the weekend, I hid in my workshop and experimented with several containers. I needed something that wouldn't look too peculiar when they looked inside my bags. After trying several tins and a large Tupperware container from the kitchen, two large Maxwell House instant coffee jars seemed about right.

I'd never seen human ashes before and was pleased to find they had been well ground to a fine powder, but I decided to sift them to be sure there were no large pieces that might block the pipe. It was just as well I did, because one or two largish bits of what looked like bone, a little under an inch across, would most certainly have caused a blockage.

I then put the ashes into the two jars — but — there was some left over. By this time, there was a fair amount of fine grey dust floating around in the air and covering the workbench. I don't know whether you've ever been lightly coated with human ash, but I didn't like it at all. So, I cleaned up as best I could, and went in to take a shower. It was fortunate I'd planned all this for the afternoon when my wife was out playing bridge with her cronies. But what to do with the spare ash and the pieces of bone? I decided to take a short walk in the country.

The dog enjoyed his walk. While he ran around vainly chasing pigeons, I found a tranquil spot in the corner of a field and reverently buried the remains behind a patch of stinging nettles near a hedge. I hoped God wouldn't mind.

I now had two glass jars and eighteen inches of copper pipe, all of which fitted comfortably into my briefcase beside my flying manual. The next problem was to choose a suitable trip and hope my other two crew members wouldn't mind. I was fairly sure I had thought everything through carefully enough. But I knew nobody would appreciate a flight deck full of ash if my plan backfired.

As it happened, my next flight was across the Atlantic to Philadelphia and, as luck would have it, Lloyd was the flight engineer. He was a placid sort of bloke who, I knew, would take in his stride the sort of caper I had in mind.

◊◊◊

'Morning Lloyd.' We shook hands and I greeted Chris, our co-pilot. Lloyd, I'd flown with many times before, but Chris, I hardly knew. I decided to wait until we were on the aircraft before telling them what was hidden in my briefcase. It was a large briefcase, one of those big square ones pilots the world over use to carry their manuals and flight documents. The crew bus took us first to flight briefing, then to the aircraft. In those days, security was not as it is now, crew bags were not searched or X-rayed, I knew my little secret would be safe. But what would Lloyd and Chris have to say when they knew?

Somehow, in all the bustle of our pre-flight preparation, I was unable to find an opportunity to tell them what I had in mind. There were too many people coming and going — refuellers, dispatchers, cabin crew and the like. It's a very busy time. All the checklists, the load sheet to be signed, the airways clearance from ATC, the take-off and then a complicated departure route to be flown. And, finally, the clearance from Shanwick Oceanic Control Centre. So, it wasn't until after we'd climbed to altitude, had passed southern Ireland and were out over the North Atlantic, that things quietened down and I felt able to tell them.

I took off my headset and turned to Chris and Lloyd. 'D'you remember that conversation Lloyd? A few months back by the coffee machine, outside my office. We were talking about Geoff Dawkins.'

'God dying on April Fool's Day?'

'Yes, that's the one.'

I looked across at Chris and started to explain. 'Geoff Dawkins, Senior Captain, Atlantic Baron and all that, long retired. His initials were G.O.D., hence his nickname. He died earlier this year in April — on the first. According to his widow, his dying wish was to have his ashes scattered in the middle of the ocean at 30^0 West, it was even in his Will. She asked me, via a mutual friend, to see what I could do. I have them here in my briefcase.'

'You're joking.' He clearly thought I was mad.

I knew I needed Lloyd's help, turning to him

I said, 'I've thought of a way. D'you remember that flight engineer who connected a vacuum cleaner hose to the sextant mounting on a VC10?'

'Oh yes,' he laughed. 'But it flipped out through the hole and flapped around on the roof making a terrible noise.'

I looked at Chris, 'Well, we have a similar mounting here. I've checked.'

He looked bemused. He'd never been a navigator, so I showed him the copper pipe and explained how I could insert it into the hole and use it to suck out the ashes. I gave the pipe to Lloyd and asked him what he thought.

'Might work, Boss,' as he examined the smoothed-over end, 'Shall I see?'

'No, better be me, in case it all goes wrong. I'll only do it if both of you agree. Think it over — if you don't like it, I won't do it.' And turning to Chris, 'I'm sure Lloyd can explain while I go downstairs and see how the cabin crew are getting on. It'll give you two a chance to talk it over.'

When I asked Annie, our stewardess, to delay our lunch, she scolded me, saying it was very inconvenient. 'That's not like you lot, I thought you gannets were always hungry.' And she chased me out of the galley.

'Looks OK to us,' this was Lloyd when I returned to the flight deck.

'But you'd better not bloody drop it,' muttered Chris.

'Thanks, I won't. Oh — and I've asked Annie to wait with our lunch. Didn't think you'd appreciate dust in your steak and kidney. How long to 30^0 West?'

'Exactly sixteen minutes.'

'When we start, Chris, all you have to do is mind the shop and give me a count down. Lloyd and I will do the business.'

'Lloyd, I think you'd better stand here between me and the flight deck door, we don't want one of the cabin crew barging in at the critical moment.' And we rehearsed how we'd do it.

'Six minutes to go,' called Chris, as he watched the INS display on the instrument panel.

I opened my briefcase and loosened the lids of the jars.

'Five minutes.'

I pushed the copper tube into the sextant mount, depressed the locking lugs and pulled the lever down to open the hole. Immediately, there was a loud roaring noise which fortunately diminished when I inserted the tube and part-closed the shutter to hold it tight.

'Right, Lloyd, you hold the tube for a moment while I open the jar.'

'Four minutes.'

I took the first jar out of my briefcase on the floor by my feet.

'Three minutes.'

Lloyd placed his bulk between me and the

flight deck door. I unscrewed the lid and held the jar up to the pipe. With a whoosh, a small tornado of ash shot up the pipe.

'Wow, like a rat up a drainpipe,' he chuckled.

I had planned to say a few words: 'Ashes to ashes, dust to dust,' or better still, 'We therefore commit his ashes to the airy deep ...' But there wasn't time.

'Two minutes.'

'Ready for lunch yet? I've got the first tray here.' Annie tried to squeeze past Lloyd. 'What on earth are you two doing? And what's all this about rats?'

'Skipper's cleaning the sextant mount. Give us a few more minutes,' said Lloyd.

She took one look at me and retreated hurriedly. Perhaps it was the mention of rats.

'One minute.'

'Right, here goes with the second jar.' Whoosh. I breathed a sigh of relief. 'And not a drop spilt.'

'OK and that's 30° West,' said Chris. 'Is the genie out of the bottle yet?'

'Like shit off a shovel,' said Lloyd.

'Yeah — couldn't see him for dust!' I removed the pipe, closed the shutter, checked the sextant mounting, made sure it was all safe and put everything back in my briefcase. 'Clean as a whistle. Thank God for that ... in a manner of speaking.'

Annie returned with the first two trays of our lunch. 'What were you two doing? Just look at you all. Like a bunch of schoolboys with guilty faces.'

'There was a funny noise,' said Lloyd with a straight face, 'Sextant holes do that sometimes. Thought we ought to check it.'

'Never heard of 'cleaning the sextant mount' before, and as for it making funny noises — that sounds very naughty!' And she bustled out like a disapproving schoolmarm. 'Well really! Do you boys ever grow up?'

Chris made a spluttering noise which might have been laughter and then busied himself calling ATC on the HF radio to give them our position report at 30^0 West while I returned to the captain's seat as though nothing unusual had happened.

Lloyd and I agreed the steak and kidney pie was exceptionally good that day. Chris said his salmon was 'alright'. Lloyd suggested that perhaps it could have done with 'a dusting of seasoning'. Chris decided he wasn't quite so hungry!

◊◊◊

When we arrived in Philadelphia, I wondered how to explain the presence in my briefcase of two dusty but empty Maxwell House coffee jars to the customs officers. To avoid any embarrassment, I hid them in a rubbish bag in the galley before leaving the aircraft — while no one was looking.

Going through customs, the man examined my briefcase. 'What's this?' He asked, 'Do you always travel with copper tubing in your bag, Captain?'

Lloyd, with a big grin on his face, leant over and explained, 'No, he normally travels in alooominum toobing.'

Back home a few days later, I phoned Barry and told him 'Mission Accomplished'. I gave him the Latitude and Longitude of where the ashes had gone overboard — exactly 52 degrees North and 30 degrees West — adding something about going up like a homesick angel. However, I decided not to tell him about the small quantity of ash and bone resting in peace behind a stinging nettle patch under a hedge in the tranquillity of rural Berkshire.

When Barry came to see me the following week to collect the urn, I asked him why 30° West was so special. He had wondered that too. Not even Dawkins' wife knew — but, he said, he'd done a little research.

Dawkins had been in RAF Coastal Command, flying B-24 Liberators searching for U-boats in the 'air gap' during the Battle of the Atlantic. At various times, he'd been based in Northern Ireland and Iceland. When a convoy was attacked in mid-Atlantic in November '42, his younger brother had gone down with his ship. The Liberators arrived too late. It seemed Dawkins had never forgiven himself for not searching a little further — out as far as 30° West.

'Perhaps,' Barry said, 'That was why he was such a stickler, so up-tight, so remote and why he drove everyone so hard.'

'Not your normal burial at sea,' I replied,

'But if that's the case I hope he's now at peace with his brother.'

On Watch

Someone is shaking my shoulder, forcing me up from that warm, comfortable oblivion. 'Wake up, wake up man!' Why? Why now? I've only been asleep for a few minutes. 'Wha's the time?' I mumble.

'Nearly 4 o'clock, you're on watch in ten minutes. You've been sleeping since midnight.'

Oh God, why am I here? Why the hell did I ever agree to go sailing again with these people? A violent lurch rolls me sideways against the hull. I hear the gurgle and swish of water racing past only inches from where I lie.

It's pitch dark, I can't see a thing. Everything is leaning sideways. Crash! The boat shudders and water splashes down the open hatch onto my face. I try to lever myself out of the bunk but another crash forces me back. I disentangle a leg from the folds of my sleeping bag, but one foot remains trapped inside.

Yet another crash rolls me out onto the bunk below, provoking a stream of obscenities from its rudely awakened incumbent. With advanced gymnastics, I avoid disturbing him further, but I slip and end up on the floor, sitting in a pool of icy water. I feel slightly sick, and wish I were home.

I've slept fully dressed, but now need to find my oilies and my seaboots before going up on deck. I'd carefully left them — somewhere — with the boots still in the trousers, so I could just step into them. I grope amongst stinking

damp oilies in the wet locker. Oh hell, someone has moved mine from the peg I left them on. And a boot is missing. Another crash and a lurch send me sprawling across the opposite bunk, provoking more curses.

It's slippery underfoot and the violent tossing about makes standing impossible. I give up and resign myself to kneeling in the puddles. At last I find my oilies, and the errant boot, but how do I now stand up to put them on? I wedge myself between the gimballed table and the forrard saloon bulkhead — and get banged on the head by the wildly swinging oil lamp.

Now, reasonably stable at last, I manage to put one leg into the oilies but they're sticky with damp. However hard I push, my leg won't go the whole way down. I feel for the corner of the bunk, sit, and worm my foot down the leg into the boot. At last — one down, now for the other. But where the hell has the other damn boot gone? I find it under the table, which decides at this point to take an almighty swing, banging the other side of my head. But I've found the boot and pull it on.

I zip up the trousers and grope for my jacket. Then — as so often — climbing out of bed raises an urgent need to pee. I hang my jacket back in the wet locker, stagger forward, squeeze through the door into the cubicle where the heads are and contemplate my next move. In a small boat, heaving around in a gale, you need at least three points of contact to avoid being thrown around — either two feet and a hand, or two hands and a foot. But how can I hold on, undo the zip, lower my oily trousers and find my willie simultaneously? Cold has an unfortunate effect upon male pride, the recalcitrant object is almost impossible to locate through layers of trousers and long-johns! So, I use my head. Placing my feet well apart, I press my own head against a deckbeam and now, with two hands free, finally undo the zip. The desire is urgent, the minute object found and —oh! — the relief!

Now, the next problem. The boat-builder, for reasons known only to himself, decided the mast should pass through the deck and down one corner of the cubicle to the keel below. So, in a space less than four feet by three, there's little room for the heads, a basin, and an unfortunate occupant. No room to bend over, much less to pull up my trousers. I open the door and lurch out into the saloon with my oilies still around my ankles. I struggle like a wounded caterpillar to pull them up, grope for my jacket and ready myself to face the tempest.

The oil lamp, swinging from the saloon skylight, lunges again at my head, but this time I avoid it and grope my way aft towards the companion way. In the dim red light over the nav table, I check the position on the chart and grin weakly at Liz — huddled in the galley — thanking her for waking me. I climb the steps, look out through the hatch and am met by a slug of cold seawater, some of which goes down my neck. Huge black mountains with white crests thunder past as the boat rises to meet them. Spray lashes my face as I step out into the cockpit. I slump onto one of the seats and, again, wonder why I'm here. 'Get yourself round this!' shouts Liz as she thrusts a mug of hot sweet tea into my hands from below.

Thud! Another wave crashes against the hull sending salt spray into my tea. Well, at least it's warm but the salt makes it taste disgusting.

'Right, Phil,' yells John at the helm, 'Let me know when you're ready to take over. We're steering two five zero, wind's steady from the northwest, and we're close hauled on starboard tack with two reefs in. She's safe enough, for the moment.'

I digest this good news as we heel further over in a gust, spilling the last of the tea down my front.

'We're about fifty miles north of the next shipping lane,' he says. 'No ships in sight, but possibly a yacht way out to port, heading the same way as us.'

Ducking down below the boom, all I can see is phosphorescent foam streaming along the lee rail and, beyond, retreating rows of white crested mountains. 'OK,' I say, 'I'm ready now.'

John stands up, allowing me to slip in behind him so I can take the tiller. We're stomping along at eight knots, bursts of spray flying over the weather bow as white horses gallop in from windward. I wedge myself against the coaming with a foot against the opposite cockpit seat. Comfortable at last (relatively speaking), I look around as John goes below.

'See you in four hours', he says as he disappears.

'You OK up there?' shouts Liz, 'I'll be on my bunk. Call me if you need me.' Sliding closed the hatch, she too disappears.

ON WATCH

I'm left on my own. John, an old flying colleague, will soon be sound asleep and, with luck, Mike, will sleep on, oblivious to my having fallen on his head. The racing mountains seem less threatening now. I'm adapting to their rhythm, easing and heaving the tiller to meet each one. Now and then a wave bursts against the bow sending phosphorescent jewels crashing into the jib. I scan round for ships, but see none, not even the yacht supposedly down to loo'ard. I am alone with the elements. I relish the solitude. Down below the others are sleeping, only Liz awake ready to be called if needed.

The wind still howls in the rigging. The clouds still race overhead, but the gale seems to be easing a little. Within minutes, the moon bursts out low on the horizon, spreading a glistening staircase across the waves. Everything is transformed, the sails glow above my head. The Pole Star appears behind me over my left shoulder. The clouds are tearing themselves apart and clearing from the west. More stars appear. Jupiter shines out from behind the mainsail and the Milky Way begins to spread its arc across the velvet blackness above.

My senses tingle, the gale heightening my sense of being alive. Now I know why I'm here. I'm at peace with the elements. All I need is my breakfast!

A Brief Encounter

I met her in the gentlemen's toilets. She was slim, almost frail looking. Dark hair, cut in a bob, framing a sad unnaturally pale face. I supposed her to be around forty — hard to tell because of the deep lines running down each side of her mouth, she may have been much younger. She was seated just inside the door smoking a cigarette. Beside her was a half full bucket of soapy water and a mop. Behind her, pinned to a board on the wall, were various notices about keeping the facilities clean and tidy, and who to call should something go wrong.

I wished her a breezy good morning, but she didn't reply, instead she looked up at me with the beautiful anxious eyes of a hare. Also on the wall, was a collection of picture postcards from various parts of the world, one of which I recognised as a map of the Falkland Islands. 'Been there,' I said. She made no reply, so I walked on down the passage to the showers in the yachtsmen's washrooms.

Our boat was moored only a few yards away across the road. We had arrived in Weymouth the previous afternoon. There were six of us on board, six men in an old wooden yawl, intending to continue west towards Ireland. But the forecast was not good. A deepening low was expected to cross the British Isles, causing force 8 to 9 gales in the Channel for the next twenty-four hours. Those familiar with this coast will know it is not a good idea to round Portland Bill in such conditions. We would be stuck here for a while.

Weymouth is a busy little harbour, lined with attractive buildings, many dating from the eighteenth century. Fortunately, we had arrived sufficiently early to secure a berth alongside the quay because, by morning, it had filled with yachts, many rafted together — all sheltering from the impending gale. Seeing so many, I was pleased to be ahead of the early morning rush for the washrooms. After the sweaty oilies and cramped conditions on board, it was so good to luxuriate in the soothing sensations of hot water running over my naked body.

The Falklands postcard sent my mind flying across the world to the bottom of the globe. Some ten years before, I had left Brize Norton on a fresh June morning in the Oxfordshire countryside — our first stop, Ascension Island in the South Atlantic. That flight had been a week of amazing contrasts.

Miles from anywhere, Ascension is a forbidding black extinct volcano, capped with an improbable green forest on its summit.

Being close to the equator, the climate is hot and humid, eased only by the gentle breezes of the southeast trades. If it were not for the solidified lava flows and jagged fields of volcanic ash, it might well have been a Caribbean island, instead it looks like an outpost on the Moon.

Our flight was a military charter. Our destination the Falkland Islands. Our mission to deliver a 747 load of squaddies to guard this lonely archipelago nearly 4,000 miles further to the south. But June in the southern hemisphere is the middle of winter. It is cold and windy, with frequent gales and snow showers. The scenery resembles the Outer Hebrides.

We landed at the newly constructed Mount Pleasant airport in a howling cross wind on a wet and slippery runway. The weather was so bad that the two F4 Phantom fighter aircraft which were supposed to have escorted us in had been unable to take off. On leaving our 747, the first things we were given were minefield maps, a lecture on the various types of mines still left lying around and stark warnings never to stray off the beaten track — and never to touch any unusual objects. The war had finished only three years before. Landmines and unexploded ordnance had not yet been cleared. But the islands are bleakly beautiful.

After my shower, I felt clean and vigorous and ready for a good breakfast. But I was still intrigued by the postcard and that long remembered journey. On my way out, I stopped by the door to take a better look.

'Falkland Islands,' she smiled. She had put away her bucket and mop, extinguished her cigarette, and was readying herself to leave. I told her about my flight down the length of the North and South Atlantic Oceans, and how much I had been struck by the haunting beauty of those islands, even in the depth of winter. I also told her how the RAF had taken me up in a Hercules around Pebble Island and then up and down Falkland Sound past San Carlos Water.

'In that case you must've passed by where I used to live,' she replied in an accent I could not quite place — West Country? A bit of Welsh perhaps and a slight antipodean lift that makes every statement sound like a question.

'Where was that?'

'Near Port Howard — West Falkland.' I admitted to not knowing where it was.

'Pretty well opposite San Carlos, you've heard of that, haven't you?'

'I certainly have. How long were you there?' I asked.

'All my life until five years ago. Born and bred there, kept sheep until that bloody war.'

'But you must have been pleased when we kicked the Argentinians out.'

'Oh — we were — but we were ruined. Ever bin anywhere after a war?'

'Only that one time.' And I told her about how we had been briefed about the mines. 'I still have the minefield map at home.'

Her brown eyes misted over. She looked forlorn and quietly began to weep. 'You've no idea. Turfed out of our house. Locked up in a barn. Our sheep eaten by Argies — or killed by mines — or lost in the camp.' A long pause. 'After it were over, we daren't go out an' look for the rest of 'em. Bloody mines an' ammo everywhere. Thousands of acres abandoned.' An even longer pause. 'An' our house trashed.'

I stood awkwardly beside her while she tried to compose herself. 'What's the camp?'

She sat for a long time with her head in her hands, then looked up at the postcard. 'It's what we call the countryside, lovely it were — until that bloody, bloody war.'

'Is that why you're here?' I asked her gently. She told me they couldn't stay, with half the land too dangerous to farm, most of the sheep either lost or blown up. 'Tragic it were, we had to put so many down. Makes you weep.' The place was no longer viable, they didn't own the farm, the work dried up, she had split up with her husband and had nowhere to go. But she did have relatives in Weymouth. 'Spent the last of my savings to come here.'

She shook her head, 'Not much of a job this — cleaning bogs.' Then looking up with a half-smile, 'From one bog to another, as it were.'

'Well, they are the cleanest yachtsman's facilities I've ever seen, not that that's much of a consolation.'

'So few people ever stop to say thank you. It weren't like that back home. We all knew each other, see. Always stopped to give people the time of day, we did.'

Not knowing quite what to do or say, I gently laid a hand on her shoulder and said, 'Look, I'm on my way to have some breakfast, you seem to have finished here, would you like to join me for a coffee or something?'

Diffidently, she looked up at me with wary eyes. But she accepted and we walked round the corner to a cafe, one that is well known to visiting yachtsmen for its enormous sailors' breakfasts. All she would have was an orange juice and a coffee. Then she told me a little more about her life. Her father, originally from New Zealand, had emigrated there in '46. Her mother was a Falklander. 'Dad knew about sheep.'

She had been born on the farm, had grown

up with sheep, dogs, horses and cattle — there was grazing for the cows near the house, and the hills behind were good for sheep. They rode most of the time because there were no real roads, so she had learnt to ride at a very early age. As in all isolated places, the people were friendly and helped each other. Shearing time was a communal activity, with boisterous parties afterwards. It was at one of these she had met a local man when she was barely twenty and fallen in love. When her father was killed in an accident, she and her new husband took over the farm, several thousand acres, and her mother stayed on. It had been a good life until the Argies arrived.

'It were peaceful an' quiet. Hard work but satisfying.' She described the simple routines of the farm. The passing of the seasons, the gales and the snow in winter, the sunlight glistening on the sea in summer. The abundant wildlife, penguins, seals and quantities of seabirds wheeling overhead. They had no television, no telephones, only radio. They didn't have any children, they made their own entertainment and read books. 'Do you read at all?'

'Yes, a lot,' I replied.

'Ever read Thomas Hardy? Life was much like that, but a much smaller community.'

I could see it all so easily. 'I was brought up on a small farm, not far from Dartmoor,' I told her, 'I guess it was much the same.'

'Bet you had better food,' she laughed.

'We ate sheep, sheep and sheep. Mutton for breakfast, mutton for lunch and mutton for dinner. That's all we knew, but it were OK. An' we grew all our own veggies.'

'It was much the same for me. After the war, World War Two that is, when I was a boy, there was still food rationing. Meat was scarce, no lamb or mutton for us, it was chicken and rabbits shot for the pot. My father ran a small chicken farm — and we grew our own vegetables too.'

We compared notes and I wondered what it would have been like had war come to Devon.

'When the war started, all hell broke loose, Argie planes low overhead, ships firing at 'em, your aircraft shooting some down — and bombs going off. Locked in that barn we couldn't see much but we could certainly hear it. We weren't released until the end, after Stanley fell.'

She was about to say more when two of my shipmates arrived. She started up, nearly spilling the remains of her coffee. 'I'd better go. Thanks, it was good to talk.'

I went with her to the door. 'I have no memories of the war, thank God,' I said. 'I was a baby when we were evacuated from Singapore. Only just in time, it greatly affected my mother. And we lost everything too. So, I have a slight inkling of what you've been through. You have my sincere sympathy. What do you plan to do next?'

'Go to New Zealand when I've saved enough

money. Where my father's family still live. They keep sheep there too.'

'I hope it works out.' And she slipped quietly away before I even had time to know her name.

Over breakfast, the others ribbed me about my girlfriend.

'It wasn't like that at all,' I explained and recounted a little of what she had told me.

'War is such a ghastly experience, not glorious at all. Here in England, all we ever heard about was how wonderful our troops were defeating the Argentinians and sending them packing. You rarely hear about the aftermath. The damage. What it means for the local people.'

Such a brief encounter. Such a different view of that distant war 8,000 miles from where we were now eating our enormous breakfasts.

I never saw her again.

A Steamy Situation

W here the hell have you been? Just look at you, bloody disgrace.' Ronnie sidled past the captain and hastened towards the back of the bus. He slumped exhausted into a seat and began to rub his face with a grimy handkerchief. He looked like a raccoon with black smudges around his eyes and nose, what hair he had stood stiffly on end, his bald pate shone with sweat which trickled down his cheeks in sinuous rivulets, and his eyes were red and watery. Attempts at removing the smuts had only made things worse. One of the stewards made jokes about his mascara running, but a kindly stewardess offered him some wipes from her handbag. Everyone else sat silently, wondering what their curmudgeonly old captain would say next.

But Ronnie's clothes were surprisingly clean — uniform trousers neatly pressed, shoes well-polished, tie in roughly the right place, though his shirt, partly hidden under his jacket, was decidedly grubby. Whatever he had been up to, he must have had little time to change before joining us in the crew bus. And here we were, having awaited his arrival, about to leave the Ikeja Arms Hotel for the airport and our flight north through Kano back to London. There were ten of us on the crew, Captain Knowles; Charlie, who was the senior first officer; John, the flight engineer; me, the junior co-pilot; and six cabin crew down the back. Knowles was known for his peppery temper, but apart from his initial outburst, he merely glowered and gazed out of the window into the blackness of the night.

We had arrived in Lagos three days before on a beautiful Monday morning. But this was July in the wet season, and anyone who has been to Nigeria during the rains well-knows what a hell hole it can be. The rain, we knew, would come — and it did. By mid-afternoon the temperature was in the nineties, thunderstorms towered overhead, and torrents of water poured from the sky onto the steaming ground beneath.

Our flight south had been without incident. Despite the January coup and reports of atrocities around Kano, we had seen nothing. On this bright sunny morning, the only obvious signs were some heavily armed troops guarding the airport and people being understandably jumpy. Fortunately, the Ikeja Arms remained an oasis of calm despite food being limited, bedrooms smelling musty, air-conditioners sounding like express trains, geckos running around the ceilings in the middle of the night

A STEAMY SITUATION

(sometimes plopping onto the beds beneath) and the water, when it could be coaxed from the taps, having a curious brownish tinge. But the Carlsberg was plentiful and cold, and the service immaculate.

There was little to do other than frequent the bar, chew your way through a steak or two in the restaurant, read books or gaze out through the rain at the swimming pool, reputed to be of Olympic size, but rumoured on good authority to be a few feet short. An oversight by the builders, some said — ran out of cement or used the wrong tape measure they joked.

Early Tuesday morning, a message came through saying the southbound flight had been cancelled, our return to London would be delayed until Thursday. When he heard this, Ronnie disappeared. 'I'll be back Wednesday,' he told me, 'Going up country, don't tell the skipper.'

Around midday, the power failed, the air-conditioning stopped, we sweated like pigs, and the telephones went up the spout. No one knew what was happening. This was not so long after the riots and civil war in the Congo — our imaginations went into overdrive. Was the same likely to happen here? This was definitely not one of my favourite stopovers.

Late Wednesday evening, the power came back on. After nearly two days with no air-conditioning, we were hot and irritable. Even the beer had become lukewarm. Another day of that would have been unbearable. Now it was Thursday, Ronnie had not reappeared, and I was worried. However, shortly before we were due to leave, he was seen exiting a car and rushing into the hotel. At least he was here, even if late for pick-up, out of breath, covered in sweat, grease and dirt.

Our rackety old bus bumped and ground its way through the night. The soldiers at the roadblock stopped us, inspected us and then waved us through towards the airport and the BOAC offices beside the low ramshackle terminal building. Ronnie kept his distance from Captain Knowles as we examined the flight plan and Met forecast. When we had finished, Knowles took Ronnie to one side for a 'talking to', I didn't hear it all, but to say he was displeased would be an understatement. It finished with, '...... and you'd better stay at the back of the flight deck where I needn't look at you. And — keep well away from the passengers.'

Knowles stayed in the office, talking to the station manager while we three walked out to prepare the aircraft. Ronnie remained rather quiet as we mounted the steps. John stayed outside to supervise the refuelling and do the outside checks, I climbed into the right-hand seat and started on the pre-flight cockpit checks, while Ronnie disappeared into the crew toilet. Laura, the stewardess who had given him the wipes, followed and offered to help remove some of the smuts. After much giggling, he reappeared little improved, but smelling strongly of Elizabeth Arden. At that point, the captain came aboard and settled himself into the left-hand seat. His temper had improved.

'Can't have that young feller sitting beside me looking as though he's climbed out of a coal hole.' A pause while he sniffed the air, 'And smelling as though he's been in a brothel.'

Ronnie remained quiet, safely out of sight at the nav table at the back of the flight deck — or at least so he thought.

Knowles turned round in his seat. 'And what exactly did you get up to?' he demanded.

Before Ronnie could reply, Laura breezed in with some bottles of cold water. 'Thought you could do with these,' she said, adding with the sweetest of smiles, 'I hope you don't mind captain, but I used some skin cleanser on Ronnie's face. It hasn't improved his looks, but it certainly makes him smell better.'

Knowles thanked her and turned again

to Ronnie, 'But you still haven't answered the question.' Before he could answer, a station officer arrived to say they were having problems processing some of the passengers, something to do with extra security checks by the army, it would take at least another twenty minutes.

Knowles looked again at Ronnie and asked what on earth he had been doing. And Ronnie began. He was a steam railway nut (he didn't exactly use those words), spending his spare time working on the Bluebell Line. They were restoring engines and in constant need of spare parts, these could only be found in scrap yards or disused British Railway work sites; most were becoming extremely scarce, especially those needed for vintage locomotives. He had been doing this for some years, starting in the workshops, then graduating to fireman and occasional engine driver. They knew Ronnie travelled frequently to Africa, where antiquated steam locomotives were still in daily use, and had asked him to see what he could find. He had scoured workshops in Nairobi and Johannesburg looking for a steam injector, but without success. On a recent trip to Lagos, he had visited the running sheds in Ebute Metta where he had struck up a friendship with an engine driver called Joshua Temilolu.

Joshua, he said, was a small man with a huge smile who loved his job. 'I told him about my work on the Bluebell Line and he showed me over his 2-8-2 River Class locomotive. Next time I came to Lagos, he said I could join him on the footplate.'

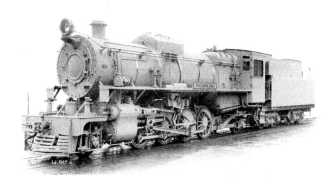

'Don't normally enjoy Lagos but this was too good to miss. First thing on Monday, when we arrived, I phoned him, but he wasn't due to drive north 'til Tuesday. Big problem, there'd be no time for a ride and be back for pick-up. That delay to our flight was a godsend, I could now go up to Ibadan, and be back on Wednesday. And I'd be able to drive. That's why I left in a hurry. Strictly against regulations, but if I met the train at Agege, he'd smuggle me on board. Bit difficult, I thought, for a lone white man on an African railway station.'

Captain Knowles exploded, 'Have you any idea how bloody dangerous that was? Our manager here says there've been massacres around Kano, refugees flooding south, cha-os everywhere — you might easily have been killed. To say nothing of being late for pick-up.'

But Ronnie was so filled with enthusiasm this hardly seemed to register, and Knowles, despite his stern views, couldn't help a little smile, 'Tell me about the steam engine.'

Clearly, Knowles knew a thing or two about steam locomotives. What had started as a strained confrontation suddenly became an enthusiastic technical discussion on things like multiple valve superheaters, floating bushes, mechanical lubricators, small ends, snifting valves, crossheads, and various other incomprehensible technical bits and pieces. I have no particular interest in steam railways, so the details escaped me.

Ronnie galloped on with his story. 'Got to the station OK. Couldn't believe the mess. Muddy puddles everywhere, crowds of people, mammies selling stuff under huge umbrellas, children, dogs, cats, goats, chickens — all running around, spilling onto the track. Easy to climb up to the footplate in all that mayhem. No one saw me. Joshua tucked me away into a corner, cracked open the regulator and began to inch the train very slowly forward. He let me blow the whistle. Nearly had to stop at a level crossing. People ignored the man frantically waving a flag to stop the traffic. Just kept on shaving past in front. Amazing no one got squashed.'

He described old women sitting on their haunches, right up close to the rails, with heaps of oranges and fruit in baskets. 'Didn't seem to notice the clouds of steam blowing over them from the cylinder drains. Couldn't have done the fruit much good.' All the other stations, he said, were equally chaotic with rows of abandoned furniture, oil drums, motor tyres, filth and other rubbish — and everywhere, the ubiquitous brown puddles.

After a while, they started to run between shanty-town huts with corrugated iron roofs. The people thinned out, Joshua said to keep blowing the whistle. 'Didn't make much difference, people still wandered all over the track, you know what they're like — all so friendly, grinning and waving as we passed.'

Soon, they were among trees and fields, and Joshua was able to increase speed. He now had time to introduce Ronnie to his fireman, 'Oluwagebimini, call him Olly'. A huge man with a round black shiny face.

'Couldn't see much of the countryside. Too much rain. Rained halfway to Ibadan. We stopped at a place called Abeokuta to take on water. Then the rain eased, and I began to see where we were going. Good thing Joshua knew the line so well. He'd had to concentrate hard.'

Olly, it seemed, was a man of few words. He had been working hard and decided it was time to make Ronnie do some shovelling. Ronnie was glad to help. 'Liddle an' offen' Olly had said, 'arll round de grate.' But he hadn't bargained for all that heat. 'They enjoyed watching me. It was exhausting — "workin" like a black,' they laughed. And indeed, I was black, covered in sweat and coal dust.'

Eventually, good old Joshua took pity on him and set him to driving, and the three of them took it in turns to fire, drive and rest. 'Not so different to the Bluebell Line really. Wait 'til I tell the boys back home!'

When they arrived in Ibadan, Ronnie had to say goodbye to his two friends, they were going on up the line to Ilorin. He was really sorry to leave them, they had both been such good fun and he admired their professionalism. He put his dirty boiler suit in a bag, found a washroom, cleaned up as best he could, and went to find his hotel. He had booked a room with the intention of spending the night and buying a ticket back to Lagos in the morning. The standard, he said, was not what he was used to, but it was alright for one night. He was thoroughly pleased with himself.

But, as always, best laid plans can go awry. When he went to the station in the morning, he was told all trains from the north were cancelled, there would be nothing coming south that night or on Wednesday. No one could say why, perhaps the rains had damaged the track near Jebba or there was some kind of trouble near Kano. This was very worrying indeed; he only had enough money on him for one night and a return ticket. If he stayed longer, he would run out — it was one or the other. Taxis back to Lagos were scarce and far too expensive. There were huge queues for the buses which looked exceedingly uncomfortable, slow, smelly and overcrowded — how was he to get back to Ikeja in time for pick-up? When he tried phoning, he couldn't get through — how was he to let us know where he was? He hung around the station all day hoping for some news. When nothing happened, he returned to the hotel to find it fully booked. The only other place for the night was a dilapidated guesthouse, friendly, but not at all comfortable.

Next day at the station, they said a train might be coming through in the morning. It was now Thursday and still the phones were not working. Time was becoming very tight. But, when midday came, a train drew in with a broadly grinning Joshua on the footplate.

'What you doin' here, man? Climb up quick.' Amidst all the hubbub on the platform Ronnie managed to slip aboard without being seen, change back into his boiler suit and take his place on the footplate. Olly soon put him to work shovelling coal. Once again, the happy Joshua and his fireman were hugely amused to watch him become almost as black as themselves.

'Got back to Agege, much later than I expected, barely had time to hitch a ride to the hotel. Lucky I got here before you left, otherwise I guess I'd have been in very hot water.'

'You most certainly would have been,' said Knowles, 'And by the look of you, you could still do with some.'

As Ronnie finished his story, the last few passengers came aboard, the doors were shut, and we busied ourselves starting the engines and preparing for take-off. We soon left the heat and the rain behind as we climbed away on the first leg of our journey to Kano, an old walled city in the Muslim north of Nigeria. Beyond it lay the Sahara. We landed, refuelled, baggage carts came and went, our ground engineer recounted some lurid stories of what had been happening around the city, and the passengers boarded, including a venerable gentleman in a red turban and colourful robes who was installed in the first class together with his entourage. An interesting place, Kano, but not during the troubles.

Now Ronnie would need to navigate by the stars across some 1,500 miles of empty desert before reaching the Mediterranean coast near Algiers. He became very busy drawing lines on charts and calculating altitudes and azimuths for his astro fixes, and using the sextant to 'shoot' the stars. At the best of times, astronomical navigation is a tiring business. By the time we reached Algiers, Ronnie was exhausted, but now within range of the radio beacons of Europe, he could fold away his charts and log, lay his head on the nav table and fall into a deep sleep. Passing Paris, he was still asleep. John whispered something to Laura when she next came into the cockpit. She laughed, fetched her lipstick and drew a large red kiss on the top of Ronnie's bald head. She then splashed some more Elizabeth Arden on his cheeks while he continued snoring quietly.

When eventually he did wake, as we crossed The Channel descending towards London, there was hardly time for him to do more than drink the proffered cup of tea and monitor the approach and landing. After shutting down the engines, we tidied up the flight deck while the passengers disembarked. Ronnie couldn't think why we were all grinning at him as he donned his uniform cap which neatly hid the bright red lipstick kiss. No one said a word.

John and I wondered what Ronnie's wife would have to say about the kiss when he arrived home. Captain Knowles chided him once more for taking such a dangerous journey, but gladly accepted an invitation for a personally guided tour of the Bluebell Line and the chance to drive a steam locomotive.

Something he had yearned to do as a boy.

East African Memories

When you drive northwest from Nairobi along the old Naivasha road, after about twenty miles you come to the edge of the Great Rift Valley. Here, the land drops steeply away to the valley floor almost a thousand feet below. I remember the first time I saw it. I stopped, left the car and walked along the top of the escarpment. The peace was astonishing, the only sounds distant voices and the gentle soughing of the wind. I remember the tangy, herby scent of grass and leaves, with a faint hint of wood smoke. But the view ... the view ... the view ... laid out before me as far as the horizon, was the plain below. I must have been able to see fifty miles, a hundred miles or, perhaps, for ever. It was a patchwork of gold and tawny browns, dotted with clumps of thorn trees and a few cattle. In the near distance, stood wooded fumaroles of long dormant volcanos, and above, in the vault of the clear blue sky, small white clouds marched purposefully off towards the west, chased by their shadows on the ground.

Somewhere in this valley, not far to the south, is the Olduvai Gorge, where the earliest remnants of primitive man were found. If this was the birthplace of mankind, I could think of no more appropriate place.

I used to fly through Nairobi frequently in the late 1960s and '70s. Nearly every time, I would hire a car, stop by this ridge on my way to Naivasha, Nakuru or Lake Elmenteita to see the pink flamingos, and walk along the escarpment to fill my senses with magic. Always, the same tawny gold in the dry season and, briefly, after the rains, a brilliant green. Such were my first impressions of Kenya.

Further to the west, lies Uganda, 'The Pearl of Africa', a country with an equable climate, abundant rain, a profusion of wildlife — birds, insects, reptiles and beasts, lush forests and grasslands, the largest lake in Africa, and the Ruwenzori — 'The Mountains of the Moon'. Everything that man could want grows in this beautiful land. Not only does it flow with milk and honey, but from it also flows the White Nile. This great river, so long a mystery, disappears into the swamps of the Sudd and joins the Blue Nile at Khartoum, bringing life to Egypt and, after a journey of over two thousand miles, finally flows into the Mediterranean. Perhaps Uganda was the Garden of Eden — that is, until Idi Amin tried to ruin it.

Before Idi did his worst, BOAC VC10s regularly flew through Entebbe on their way to and from points south. The airport lies on the north shore of Lake Victoria, almost exactly on the Equator. Some seventy miles to the east lies the source of the Nile. When it was first discovered, in 1862, the river tumbled out of the lake over spectacular falls. Unfortunately, these are now drowned by a hydro-electric dam a little further downstream, but it is still a mythic place to visit. On days off, I frequently drove there to ponder the problems and privations suffered by the early Victorian explorers — Burton, Grant, Speke and Baker — all searching for the source of this mighty river.

Then one day I decided to see a real waterfall — the Murchison Falls. I hired a car, persuaded the flight engineer and one of the stewardesses to join me, and consulted on what to do should we meet a rhino round a corner. Driving north out of the city, the busy streets and shanty-town suburbs soon gave way to exuberant trees, fields and banana plantations. When the tarmac stopped, we continued on unpaved murram roads, their bright red colour contrasting vividly with the lush green vegetation on either side. The long rains were still a month away, the road was dry, and the few cars we met trailed long clouds of fine red dust, everything was covered with it. Soon, so were we.

We wound our way through scattered woodland, hoping on every turn to meet an elephant, but all we saw were cannonball size droppings in the road. It was not until we came out onto the plain that we found wildlife in abundance — elephants far away, and quantities of buck, deer and eland, a herd of buffalo, but no giraffes or lions. In the distance were the low hills towards which we were driving and beyond, a huge thunderstorm.

As we neared the hills, we entered more forest. Recent rain glistened on the leaves and grass. The rough track became slippery. The air was heavy with the glorious pungent smell of freshly dampened earth. Then we were there, at the top of the falls. Before us, the whole Nile thundered, boiled and plunged through a gap in the rocks no wider than a stone's throw down into the gorge 130 feet below. No sign of human activity could be seen other than a low pipe rail fence.

It was one of the most magnificent natural sights I have ever seen. Dark rocks on either side of white water, clouds of spray, trees and hills glistening clean, lit by the sun behind us. Beyond, a blue-black thunderstorm filling the whole sky. Shafts of lightening, the roar of water, and the rolling reverberations of thunder.

To an ant-like human being, walking upon the surface of the Earth, this had to be a creation of the gods rather than of nature. Did Thor or Zeus travel south to cleave the rock and unleash the Nile to take water to the Pharaohs? Or was it some unnamed African god? And did Wagner write the thunderous music of the heavens in the clouds above?

A Country Gent

I knew of him, of course. Everyone did. But I'd never flown with him. Seen him in hotels down the routes — on one occasion holding forth at length to his crew in Nairobi. As a senior first officer on the fleet, one of my amusements was to study the quirks of the various captains I flew with. Charles Squires would be an interesting addition to my collection.

He was a short rotund man, with a round face, dark hair combed across his bald head, slightly protuberant eyes and a wide mouth. Self-importance, like his belly, went before him; behind his back people said he resembled Mr Toad. He was amiable enough, always trying to help, but not quite succeeding.

People tended to avoid him, if possible. So long as you pretended to listen to his stories with interest, they said, and so long as you tolerated tedious descriptions of his country abode, or explanations of how things should be done, he remained perfectly happy — even when his audience barely failed to conceal their boredom. It was fortunate he was so self-absorbed, he seemed never to notice.

I looked forward to flying with him — 'furthering my studies,' I told myself — and one day I did. It was a long trip through Rome and Nairobi down to Jo'burg and back. At Crew Reporting in London, Charlie was late, very late, so the three of us — Ralph, the flight engineer; John, the junior co-pilot, and me — we decided to complete the flight planning on his behalf. As second-in-command, I said I would wait in the office until he arrived while they went out to the aircraft to do the pre-flight checks. The roster clerk was about to call out the standby captain when a very flustered Charlie rushed in full of apologies, saying he'd been held up on the A4 near Marlborough. I told him we had prepared everything for the first leg to Rome, the weather was OK, a suitable fuel figure had been agreed, and the flight engineer was out at the aircraft ready to load more, should he so decide. Charlie, bless him, was most grateful for all of this and accepted our decisions without demur.

While we walked out to our VC10, he began to explain, 'I live near Bath, you know, an exceedingly good area. Lovely countryside. Good social life. But it is rather far to drive. I have a fast car, you know, Daimler Sovereign, better than the Jaguar XJ6, very comfortable for long journeys.'

As he started on the virtues of the straight-six engine and the plush interior, we reached the aircraft. Fortunately, this brought to a halt details of dual overhead camshafts and the like. With suitable apologies, we threaded our way past the passengers gathering around the forward steps ready to board. Charlie, as always, was the very model of politeness.

Ralph and John had completed the checks — the navigation aids were tuned to the desired radio beacons, the flight instruments set to the correct headings and bearings for our departure, altimeters set as required, take-off speeds calculated and marked up, and the airways charts carefully folded and placed on Charlie's seat in the order in which he would need them. He thanked us graciously, but unlike most captains, went straight back to the galley to talk to Graham, the chief steward.

'From what I can hear,' said Ralph leaning forward from the engineer's seat to whisper in my ear, 'Sarah is not best pleased.'

She burst onto the flight deck, 'Will someone please get that damned captain back into his seat where he belongs. He's fussing about and getting in the way of the passengers!' Sarah, our stewardess in the first class, was known not to mince matters.

With only ten minutes to go, dear old Charlie climbed into the left hand seat and started his pre-flight briefing. I have to say, despite the rush of his arrival, missing the flight planning and his seeming lack of attention to the flight preparation, he flew the take-off and departure immaculately.

It was an unusually clear evening over most of Europe with only a hint of gathering mist in the valleys. Paris slid slowly towards us, prompting Charlie to pick up the PA. 'Those of you on the right-hand side will have an excellent view of the city,' I heard him say, followed by a lengthy explanation of the various sights that could be seen from our lofty perch. I wondered how much they could really see, looking into the glare of the setting sun.

But later, as we approached the Alps, the view was truly magnificent; the mountain tops lit in gold, their glistening peaks contrasting vividly with the deep blue shadows in the valleys below. And, dominating everything, the golden pyramid of the Matterhorn. Again, Charlie seized the opportunity to talk to the passengers. He told them where we were, gave them a long description of what he could see, ending with details of our route towards Elba and Rome. By the time he stopped we were over the valley of the Po, heading towards Genoa.

'Captain,' John interjected when Charlie had finished, 'Here's the latest weather for Rome. That low over the Gulf of Genoa's pushed further east, looks as though the cold front is over Fiumicino. They're reporting strong winds and rain, and Ciampino isn't much better. Twenty knots straight across the runway with heavy showers.' And he passed Charlie the details he had copied down from the VOLMET weather broadcast.

Charlie quietly absorbed this information and briefed us for the descent and arrival on runway 16L. Halfway down, we ran into cloud and heavy rain. The approach was particularly bumpy, with Charlie struggling to follow the ILS instruments that aligned us on the centre line towards the runway. When we broke cloud, the approach lights were some way off to the right, but now that we were visual, he executed a smart 'S' turn and touched down in exactly the right place. He went up in my estimation, even though I had wondered how much of the struggle was due to the weather and how much to Charlie's erratic instrument flying. Like many of the old boys, he had trouble flying on instruments, but was good once he could see the runway.

The hotel we stayed in was the Qirinale on the Via Nazionale. Built in 1865, it oozed a faded charm unknown in most hotels used by airline crews today, but back in the '60s and '70s, we were often accommodated in fine hotels around the world. Charlie basked in the old-fashioned splendour, faded carpets, grand staircase, high ceilings and marble bathrooms. The hotel had other virtues too — it was only a short walk from a very acceptable wine bar and, for those with a more cultural bent, the Forum.

I saw little of the others during our short stay. Instead, I awoke early and walked through the near empty streets to see my favourite Roman building, the Pantheon. I followed this with a light lunch, a glass of wine and a long siesta to be ready for the flight south through the night to Nairobi.

We took off at dusk and started down the coast towards the toe of Italy. At top of climb, Charlie decided he would dine in the first-class cabin, there were spare seats and it would be more comfortable. He could safely leave the three of us to watch over the flying. On this sector, John was co-piloting, and I was navigating. As I'd already prepared my charts ready for the navigation sector over the desert, I had little to do until we reached Benghazi, so I left the nav table and joined John at the front in Charlie's vacated seat.

'Didn't see you this morning, where did you go?' he asked. 'We were trapped by Charlie at breakfast.'

'Yeah,' chipped in Ralph. 'And did he drone on about his car — Daimler this and Daimler that, classy finish, comfy seats for the long drive from his mansion in Bath. "The Queen has a Daimler you know." Couldn't bloody stop him.'

'Then he started on about the engine, how smooth it was, how quiet and powerful,' added John. 'I couldn't help pointing out it was only a Jaguar tarted up a bit.'

'Did he give you a lecture on the virtues of dual overhead camshafts?' I asked.

'Oh yeah, we got all of that, but I foxed him

on desmodromic valves, he hadn't a clue,' laughed Ralph.

'And I made a joke about dromedaries,' said John. 'Which added to the confusion.'

The conversation drifted on between making our position reports to ATC. Nearing Benghazi, John called Tripoli ATC and I sent a message back to Charlie saying we'd soon be crossing the coast.

'Do we really want to hear more about his car?'

'Don't be too hard on him,' I cautioned. 'He's harmless enough, we'll all be boring old farts when we're ancient.'

'Who's ancient?' enquired Charlie as he reappeared.

'All of us one day, skipper. We'll be over Benghazi in five minutes and I need to start navigating. Here's your seat back, I've been keeping it warm for you.'

Charlie, again, was gracious with his thanks.

Astro navigation requires precision — in calculation, in observing the stars through the periscopic sextant and when plotting the results. You have to do this for each fix and keep repeating the process every thirty minutes until within range of the ground navigation aids near destination. Even the smallest arithmetical error or miss-identification of a star will ruin the result. This requires a cool head to sort out — it is as much an art as a science. It's also hard work, but I relished it, knowing that what I was doing was the culmination of a long tradition extending back to Captain Cook and, before him, Arab seafarers using kamals in the Indian Ocean.

But back to Charlie. What with 'shooting' stars and drawing lines on charts, I only heard snatches of conversation — horses, country estates, ancient mansions and Lord Somebody-or-other. When we arrived in Nairobi, I was knackered; bed called and I slept through until late afternoon when rain, thundering down on the roof, woke me up. I ordered some tea and sandwiches in my room and read for a while. At six, I showered and went to look for the others.

In those days, the Norfolk Hotel was a long, low, red-tiled, mock-Tudor style building. At the front, a covered entrance led from the road into the reception area which, in turn, opened onto a garden at the rear and a bar and dining room to the right. The spacious dining room was fronted by a row of French windows allowing easy access to the stoep — a long veranda furnished with comfortable wicker chairs and tables. It was one of the main watering holes of old Nairobi and, naturally, much frequented by BOAC flight crews.

Even in this modern jet age, vestiges of 1930's colonial elegance lingered on, as did certain hierarchical customs. Captains stayed in comfort in the main building. We, lower mortals, were accommodated in the utilitarian addition to the rear beside the garden. The cabin crew stayed in another hotel in town.

I wandered through to the stoep and found Charlie sitting at the far end — on his own.

'Seen John and Ralph?' I asked.

'Not yet. Can I get you a beer?'

'Yes please, a cold Tusker.'

We sat for a while sipping our beers. It was the time of the long rains. Water was still dripping from the eaves. Bulbuls twittered in the trees. Light traffic swished past along the road outside. White-gloved waiters hovered in the dining room. Charlie remained uncharacteristically silent.

'When we were coming down over the desert, I thought I heard you telling the others about horses. You into riding?'

'Yes, we have some land, you know, twenty acres of pasture a few miles south of Box — near Bath, you know. My wife keeps horses. We hunt. Lord Deddleigh's estate has some very good hunting country.'

'I didn't know you rode.'

'Oh yes, the wife's very keen.'

'You do surprise me.' Images of Thelwell's sporting prints came to mind.

'Colin's a close neighbour, you know, see him often. Go round for drinks and things. Good egg, very popular in the village. They have a large country house, Christopher Wren — and several hundred acres. '

I doubted the Christopher Wren part, 'And your house?'

'Old farm house, Elizabethan in places, Georgian front, large entrance hall, drawing room, dining room, six bedrooms, a kitchen with scullery and boot hole behind. You need things like that in the country, you know.

I nodded, seeing visions of photos in *Country Life* and *Homes & Gardens*, but said nothing.

'There's a yard at the back — cobbled, with stabling and garages for three cars. The wife has a Land Rover and horsebox — and a Morris Minor Traveller for running about, one of those estate types with wood trim.'

'Much garden?'

'On old walled kitchen garden, espaliered fruit trees and Victorian glass houses. We like our food. A retired gamekeeper from the estate helps with the gardening. Colin sends over pheasants. I don't shoot, but he knows we like game.'

'Sounds very comfortable.'

'Oh, it is,' replied Charlie with warmth. 'We have one of those large four-oven AGA cookers, does the cooking, heats the kitchen and the hot water too. Of course, we also have an oil-fired central heating boiler — runs off the same oil as the AGA.'

'Another beer?' I asked.

'Thank you, shall we take them into dinner?'

I was not sure I really wanted to dine with Charlie that night, but it was still raining outside, curry was on the menu, and it would have been churlish to leave him on his own. He talked on about Colin and his estates, not only the one near Bath, but also in Scotland. Clearly The Hunt was a great leveller. Gradually I put two and two together and realised that Colin was Lord Deddleigh, I wondered what he called him to his face. Charlie was in an expansive mood. I hesitated to ask.

'They have a Daimler too, you know, not like mine, a '68 Majestic.' I then got the works about the V8 engine.

Charlie much enjoyed the curry. 'Of course, the wife makes excellent curries. We like them hot, so does Colin. He used to be in Delhi. Knows his curries. Knew the Viceroy too — Lord Louis Mountbatten, you know.'

I wasn't sure I really needed to know and, after dinner, made an excuse to take myself off to bed, saying we had an early start in the morning — I could do with my beauty sleep.

Next day, before we took off, as I was checking through the manuals, I found a new flight crew notice warning us that, after the recent hijacks, we should keep the flight deck door locked.

'Typical office,' exclaimed Ralph, 'Don't they know it's frangible. All a hijacker has to do is lean on it. Bloody silly idea, look,' and he gave it a firm push to show how much it bent. 'Any harder and my fist would go through.'

It was true. The door was designed so that if it jammed after a crash, the flight crew could break through and escape. Hijacks and doors then became the main topic of conversation on the way down to Jo'burg — should we or shouldn't we lock it? Opinions were divided. Charlie was in favour of keeping it locked. Graham asked how were the cabin crew to let us know when they needed to come in. Sarah said we would all go hungry if we didn't let *her* in. Ralph didn't like the idea of having to keep jumping up to unlock the door each time. And I said it would interrupt the navigation if I was in the middle of an astro shot. We all agreed it was impractical.

But, two days later, when we assembled for the flight north back to Nairobi, Charlie was firm. He asked Sarah and Graham to join us on the flight deck and told us we would keep the door locked throughout the rest of the trip. He had devised a system of knocks so we would know if it was a legitimate crew member wanting to enter, and he demonstrated — 'one, two, three, a pause, and then two more'. He asked us all to try it, then he sat in his seat and asked Graham to knock on the door as instructed to see if he could hear it. Satisfied with the result, and despite our protests, he instructed John, who would be in the nav seat, to lock the door once we had completed the pre-take-off checks.

It was my turn to fly, I took off and headed north for the four-hour flight to Nairobi. On reaching cruising altitude, Charlie, well satisfied with his idea, announced that he was going back into the cabin to take his breakfast in comfort. John carefully locked the door behind him before joining me at the front in Charlie's vacated seat.

'I'm a little deaf these days,' said Ralph.

'What do you mean?'

'Well — I mightn't hear him knock.'

However, 'tap, tap, tap — pause — tap, tap' and Ralph opened the door for Sarah with our breakfast trays.

'I can see you boys know which side your bread's buttered on,' she said.

A little later she tapped again and came to clear the trays away. 'Anything else while I'm here? I'll leave the teapot so you can help yourselves.'

Half an hour before top of descent, we heard the tapping code again, it was Graham asking how long to go. Sarah followed him in to clear the cups and we all complained about the ridiculousness of Charlie's system.

'How is he?' I asked.

'Finishing his coffee and boring the pants off a passenger sitting beside him.'

Ralph again locked the door when they left. Top of descent came, and I started down towards Nairobi — still no Charlie.

'Perhaps a hijacker has tied him up,' volunteered Ralph hopefully.

Then, 'tap, tap — pause — tap, tap, tap'. We waited. And again, the wrong series of taps were repeated several times.

'Think it's him?'

'Dunno. Could be. Perhaps the silly old fool has forgotten his own code,' joked Ralph, listening at the door. The tapping became louder, and we could clearly hear Charlie shouting to come in.

'I think we'd better have pity on him,' I said as we passed twenty-five thousand feet. 'I'm sure it's him.'

Bang! The door burst open and Charlie shot in. 'What the hell do you all think you are playing at? Couldn't you hear me knocking?'

'Wrong taps, Sir' said Ralph, 'Weren't sure if it was you or a hijacker. Trying to decide when you broke the door down. Lucky I hadn't got the fire axe out! And now look at what you've done to the lock.'

'At least you've proved it's frangible,' I added under my breath, as Charlie climbed back into the captain's seat.

Nothing more was said while I continued the descent towards the airfield. After landing, Charlie took me to one side and asked why we had not let him in. I explained he had used the wrong code of knocks and we were debating what may have happened. I didn't tell him we knew perfectly well it was him all along.

Ralph and the ground engineer bent the lock back into some sort of shape, but within Charlie's hearing, the subject of locks was not mentioned again for the rest of the trip. However, word spread, and I began to wonder if we had behaved rather childishly. We all have our idiosyncrasies, perhaps, we'd been too harsh. And, next time I flew, I saw that the flight crew notice had been withdrawn.

SKY TALK 2

◊◊◊

It was some months later, while I was driving down to Bristol that I noticed the A4 ran through Box village. The little devil inside me began to talk. What about seeing where Charlie lived? Had he been spinning a yarn about his life in the country? After hearing so much about it I was curious. Did he really ride? As I drove through Box, I saw the Post Office in the High Street, I had time to spare, so went in to ask if anyone knew where Captain Squires lived. Yes, they said, take the road towards Devizes, after a mile or so, turn right, don't mix it up with Great Chalfield Manor. You can't miss it. Of course, I did, and had to ask again — several times. Eventually I came to a road which ran through delightful countryside alongside a high drystone wall. I guessed it must enclose an estate of some size, but I still couldn't find Charlie's house. Then I came to a handsome four-square building, most definitely dating from the eighteenth century. It really was a fine example of Georgian domestic architecture — perfect proportions, Bath stone walls, grey slate roof, centrally placed front door with white painted sash windows above and symmetrically on either side. It seemed I had found the gentleman's country mansion so vividly described by Charlie during our African journey, except for one small detail — a discrete sign showing it to be The Deddleigh Arms Hotel.

I went in and enquired about Captain Squires' house. You've missed it, they said, couple of hundred yards back along the way you've come, at the end of the stone wall, on the left.

What I found was not quite what I expected. It was smaller than Charlie had led me to believe. The walls were built of the local honey-coloured stone, the roof was covered with Cotswold stone tiles, and strangely high peaked gables stood above mullion windows down one side, while sash windows adorned the front. A gravel path led from the road gate towards a Georgian style porch — a modern addition? This hotchpotch of styles gave the impression of a much-altered lodge house. A field gate gave access into a yard on one side, with two barns in the shape of an 'L', one arm being a stone built original, the other, one of those wooden buildings you see advertised in *Country Life*. An old Land Rover stood outside.

I gave the large lion-headed door knocker some hearty raps, but received no answer. I followed the path around the house into the yard, the stable door was open, but no horse, no Daimler and no Morris Minor. Perhaps, they had gone riding.

Suddenly, a loud crunch of gravel behind me made me start, and I turned to watch a girl in a long hippie-style caftan emerge from a bright red Mini Cooper. Chelsea by way of the Cotswolds.

'Mum, Is Dad around?' Then, looking me over, 'Who are you?'

I introduced myself saying I was a flying colleague and that I had recently flown with Captain Squires. 'Have I come to the right house?' But she looked past me towards the barns.

'That you, Chloe? I'm dying for some tea, be an angel and make some.' A tall woman appeared out of the stable, wheeling a barrow full of muck. She wore a tatty old Barbour jacket, brown corduroy trousers, wellington boots and a paisley-pattern green headscarf. Despite her untidy appearance, she had the practical elegance and commanding presence so many ladies in that part of the world possess. 'And for your friend there,' she added.

'He's not my friend.' Then, turning to me, 'But do come in anyway, Mum won't be long, she's just mucking out.'

Neither woman looked the sort who might be attracted to a man like Charlie, they both had the slender looks of good breeding. I followed Chloe's flowing robes and golden hair into the kitchen. It had a low ceiling with white painted beams, white walls, a row of white painted cupboards down one side, a Butler sink under the window, and a scrubbed pine table in the middle standing on the terracotta tiled floor. It was a comfortable, homely place, but I could see no AGA.

'Do sit down. Hope you don't mind builders. It's tea bags and mugs in this kitchen. Milk and sugar? Don't touch sugar myself. Milk's in the fridge. D'you fly with Daddy often? Sounds awfully glamorous. What's he like to fly with, do tell? I find most pilots such terrible bores, always talking about 'planes. Do you?

After this breathless monologue, slightly nonplussed, I searched for the right words. 'He's very competent, but he does talk a lot about his cars and horses.'

She snorted, 'Mum's horses, Daddy's cars!'

'Does he ride?'

'Not if he can help it, says they don't steer like 'planes. You should see him, yanking away at the reins, swearing like hell and shouting they won't turn and don't have any brakes. Horses all ignore him.'

Mrs Squires came in, bringing with her a whiff of horse manure, despite leaving her boots outside and having washed her hands. I stood up as she entered. 'Do excuse me barging in on you like this,' I offered, 'I did knock, I was looking for Captain Squires.'

'Charles? 'Fraid you've missed him, he's away at the moment, somewhere in Africa, I think. I'm Helen, by the way, Charles' other half. Glad to see Chloe's looking after you. '

'I'm a colleague, on VC10s, I flew with him recently. Down to Johannesburg.'

'He loves going there — for the golf. The Wanderers Club. Do you play?'

'No, not much of a sportsman. He says you hunt.'

'A bit, I mostly hack these days. Over the

estate behind the house — Lord Deddleigh's land. He doesn't mind as long as I keep the gates shut.'

'Mummy's being very modest, she used to ride point to points. And was very good at it too.'

'And you?' I asked.

'No time these days. I live in London — much more exciting. Only come down here occasionally to see how the oldies are.'

'Really Chloe, neither of us are that old. And look at your father, flies round the world, sits on important committees and will soon be flying Concorde.'

'I know, I know.' And looking at me, 'Daddy's on some sort of Concorde development committee, goes to Bristol a lot.'

That was news to me. I mumbled something about them being very lucky to have him and decided not to suggest that Charlie might have a problem if he continued to spend so much time in the cabin.

I thanked them both for the tea and said I needed to be on my way again, I had to be at a meeting in Filton first thing in the morning.

'That's where Charles goes.'

I excused myself, saying I was so sorry to have missed Charles, taking care not to call him Charlie. As I drove away, I mused on what I had seen. Chloe would most certainly have been an adornment on the King's Road. Helen was a down-to-earth country woman, giving every impression of being comfortable in her skin, and most unlikely to tolerate any nonsense. I wondered what she saw in Charlie — a man always attempting to be something he was not. Did he believe his fantasies, or was he trying to keep up with the Colins of this world?

But, he was a kindly man, unfailingly polite, always trying to be helpful, even if he was given to a little boasting. And me? How did others see me? A cynic, overly critical, superior, and a little arrogant perhaps?

Was Charlie the better man?

The Missionary

The telephone rang, 'Mr Chalmers is here, shall I send him in?' 'Yes please, and ask him if he would like a coffee or something.' The door opened and Keith Chalmers came in. Captain Bill Ramsey remained seated and waved him towards the chair in front of his desk. The young man looked nervous, as well he might. It is not often a pilot is summoned for an interview with his flight manager.

Anne, Ramsey's secretary, brought in two coffees, a white one with two sugars for Chalmers and the usual black for the boss. 'Sugar's in already, just as you asked,' she said, placing the cups carefully on the desk before slipping quietly away.

The flight manager lowered his glasses and carefully examined the man sitting in front of him. He noticed the thin sheen of sweat on his forehead, 'I expect you are wondering why I asked to see you.'

'Is it about that sim check I did last week?' Chalmers knew he hadn't done well and was half expecting this.

'Partly.' Ramsey would have liked to be blunt, instead, he decided a gentler approach would be better. 'I would like you to cast your mind back to a flight you did with Captain Harcourt — Last month — To Bahrain — Do you remember it?'

That was not the question Chalmers was expecting.

But it was the question that was weighing upon Ramsey's mind. It had come to his notice about a year before, when a captain he knew well, tipped him off about Keith. 'Bill,' he had said, 'You need to do something about young Chalmers, I was with him recently on a trip out east. He talked about religion and his beliefs, he even handed out some religious tracts, but soon started berating us about our sinful ways. Now, I don't mind people holding strong views, I'm very much in favour actually, but his lecturing us while we are flying is not good. Gets people's backs up. Creates a bad atmosphere. Could be dangerous with the wrong captain.'

Ramsey made a note and sent out a few feelers, as he always did in such cases. It soon became apparent that others had been upset — not to the extent of having a row, but certainly enough to create disharmony. He hesitated at first about doing anything. Instead, he would wait and watch. Over the years during which he'd been a flight manager, he had heard many rumours, most of which could be ignored. It does not do for the boss to go in heavy handed too quickly. You needed hard evidence before taking any action and, only then, might it be necessary to act — wisely and proportionately. But recently, a letter had arrived from Captain Harcourt saying he objected most strongly to being preached at by First Officer Chalmers while he was flying, and he most certainly did not like being labelled an atheist in a most offensive manner. Chalmers had been rude, he wrote, showing no respect. He recommended an interview. Ramsey knew Bob Harcourt of old, a crusty sort who was inclined to be a little pugnacious at times and very judgemental. He wondered where the truth might lie, probably fifty-fifty, you never knew. So, he phoned the flight engineer who had been with them on the trip and discovered there had indeed been quite a ding-dong, mainly caused by Harcourt over-reacting, but equally, by Chalmers provoking him, banging on needlessly about the lack of faith amongst his colleagues, their sinful behaviour and how they needed to turn to Jesus.

It was this that had prompted Ramsey to call Chalmers in for the interview. He asked Personnel to send over the personal file and then carefully examined his training file. There was little in the personal file other than a summary of his initial selection assessment, which was good, dates of various postings and promotions, the standard forms showing salary details, and a letter from a satisfied passenger commending him for being so helpful during a long delay in Accra, saying Mr Chalmers had gone out of his way to reassure an anxious family. Contrary to popular belief, a pilot's personal file contains little of interest, unless he happens to be a regular miscreant.

But the training file showed a distinct deterioration in his flying standards during the last year, together with some adverse comments about his technical knowledge. That, and his recent marginal simulator check, gave Ramsey all the ammunition he needed.

Ramsey watched the young man sitting on the other side of his desk and passed him Captain Harcourt's letter. He waited for Chalmers to read it, then asked him what he thought about it. Chalmers looked puzzled and took his time before answering. 'Yes. We did have a discussion — about Christianity, about sinful behaviour — nothing controversial. Then Captain Harcourt said Muslims have stricter rules about such things, were they better? I said, no, they weren't, because they didn't worship the same God as us, they needed to be converted to Christianity. But Captain Harcourt said both religions did worship the same God, only they used different names. I disagreed. I told him Islam is fundamentally different, Allah is most certainly not God. Then he took exception to something I said about dissolute behaviour, he took it personally and gave me a real telling off. I thought he was most unreasonable.'

Ramsey remained silent for a few minutes; he was well aware of some fairly wild room parties down the routes which a sensitive religious man might term dissolute. But he could easily see a man like Bob Harcourt jumping to the wrong conclusions. 'It's not only Captain Harcourt who is complaining about you, others on the fleet are saying similar things. There's quite a lot of talk, in fact.'

'That can't be true, I'm not like that. You know what rumours are like. I'm sure you haven't had any other letters or formal reports. Have you?'

'No, but quite a few people have dropped into my office to talk about you. And, after Captain Harcourt's letter, I 'phoned some of the men you've flown with recently — most make similar comments. Some have hinted that your discussions could be seen as offensive and provocative, possibly even dangerous.'

'That's most unfair,' he exploded, 'I do not provoke arguments. Yes, I know I have strong views. I can't help it if people disagree. I believe in God, my faith is in Christ, I'm proud to be a Christian. What's wrong with that?'

'Nothing,' Ramsey answered mildly. 'We are all entitled to our own views and beliefs. Years ago, I remember being advised never to discuss politics, sex or religion at dinner parties. Of course, it all depends on who you're with, but those subjects are likely to provoke arguments, particularly if someone feels their own beliefs are being threatened.'

'But I never threaten anybody.'

'Perhaps not, and I certainly don't think you mean to, but others may feel it.' He went on to discuss how, when someone passionately expounds their deeply held beliefs, especially on religion and politics, it can feel very threatening to those who don't share them. Had he ever tried listening to himself, or asking his colleagues what they thought of him? 'It doesn't do to trample on other people's feelings and taboos. The problem with politics and religion, is that these things are personal, they may even be the core of someone's identity. With questions of faith — and matters of belief — there is no proof. When someone feels their identity is being challenged, they are likely to react strongly.'

'But we have the proof, it's written in the Bible.'

'Others will say similar things about their holy books — the Koran, the Hindu Vedas and the Buddhist Sutras. Which of them is correct?'

'But there's only one true God.'

'Now you sound like a Muslim.' At that, Chalmers launched into a long lecture on the need to bring Christianity to the heathen. Ramsey sat back and let him talk himself out. Silence is often a good ploy. When he finally stopped, Ramsey said, 'I think you have proved my point.'

'What do you mean?'

'As a manager, my only interest is in the safety of our flight operations. Your religious beliefs — and mine for that matter — and even more importantly, those of your colleagues, all need to be respected. They should never become a bone of contention on the flight deck. I want all our crews to work as a team, the more harmoniously the better. Heated outbursts of the sort you have just displayed are not conducive to good relations and are likely to interfere with a safe operation. Do you understand that?'

'Yes, of course. But it was Captain Harcourt who attacked me.'

'Did he?' Ramsey paused to let his question sink in. 'When I received his letter, I 'phoned Les Boyd, the engineer on your trip. He tells a slightly different story. He says Captain Harcourt certainly over-reacted to your sermons. But it was you who started it, you who provoked him, and it was you who became very heated — as you have done just now. If this was only an isolated incident, I would treat it as just one of those things. But it isn't. I want you to think very carefully about your behaviour, and I want you to know that it must stop. Incidents of this sort have no place on the flight deck. You are becoming a danger to yourself and to your passengers and crew.'

Chalmers listened and would have liked to explain but realised he might overstep the mark. As a Christian, he really was offended by the drinking culture and bad language of some of his colleagues. When he tried to point this out, many of them disagreed, and he was absolutely sure he had never directed any such accusation at Captain Harcourt. He had been misunderstood and given no time to explain. But now, he thought, it was better to keep quiet.

'Which brings me to the second reason for asking you to come and see me today. Your last simulator check.'

Ramsey opened the training file. 'For most of your career with us you have done well, but I see that recently there have been several comments about your lack of technical knowledge. Do you have anything to say about that?'

Chalmers cogitated, searching for an answer. After a long pause, he said, 'The instructor was unfair. He kept asking me questions and didn't give me time to think.'

'What kinds of questions?'

'Memory items, various limitations, that sort of thing. But it was all so quick fire, it scrambled my brains.'

'But those are all things you should have at your fingertips — all the time — they're all things that require an immediate response in an emergency. In an aircraft, you don't have time for scrambled brains.' At which point, Chalmers complained about the instructor's intimidatory attitude.

'Don't you think that people may feel the same about you when you discuss religion?' But Chalmers didn't see the connection.

'Look here,' Ramsey continued, 'we're not talking about isolated incidents. There have been too many complaints about you, and too many reports about your poor technical knowledge. That is why I am obliged to take them seriously.'

Chalmers looked surprised and was about to say something when Ramsey asked, 'When was it that you began to take such a serious interest in religion and feel the need to talk about your faith?'

'I've always been religious. I was brought up a Baptist and we go to the Evangelical Baptist Church in Windsor. Two years ago, a pastor from Uganda came to talk to us, he said it was not enough to remain passive, we must go out into the world, proudly declaim our faith and convert others. He was such a good man, I was convinced.'

'But not on the flight deck,' Ramsey countered, noting to himself that this sudden change of direction seemed to coincide with the decline of his technical standards. Was Chalmers being distracted by his newfound religious fervour?

'Look, you are a serious man, it's clear you think deeply about things, so I would like to pose a serious question. How would you feel if there was an accident caused by your lack of knowledge and people were killed, but you survived? Think about it carefully. You know in your heart that those people died because of your failure. You know it was your fault. How would you live with yourself for the rest of your life, knowing that to be the case?'

Chalmers had no answer.

'I'm going to do three things. The first is to require you to have a question-and-answer session with one of our instructors to probe your technical knowledge. It will be one month from now to give you time to study the manuals. The second is to roster you for a route check, I'll choose a long trip, so the check captain has time to see how you handle yourself. And the third is to give you a warning. Today is not a formal interview, it's an informal bollocking. However, if there is a next time, it will be formal, records will be placed on your personal file and, if necessary, it may ultimately lead to disciplinary action. Now, I'm sure you have enough common sense to avoid anything like that.'

With that Ramsey terminated the interview and ushered Chalmers to the door. He shook his hand and advised him to contemplate the question — seriously. A month later, Chalmers passed the technical question-and-answer session with flying colours. He also did well on his route check, and Ramsey received no more adverse comments.

However, six months after that, Ramsey received a call from Sheila Harris, the personnel manager. Chalmers, she explained, had given her a letter, putting in his resignation, could she come and discuss it? Of course — and he suggested, instead, he come down the corridor to her office, the walk would do him good, and together, they could decide what else might be required.

Sheila showed him the letter, it was straight forward enough, he wished to resign from the airline and join the Missionary Aviation Fellowship (MAF), an organisation flying missionaries and medical supplies to remote villages in Central Africa. MAF were keen to have him, subject to a suitable reference. 'Would you be happy to write one?' Sheila asked.

Ramsey said he would be delighted to, but was there something else on her mind?

'Yes, there is. He and I had a long talk about him wanting to do God's work where it was most needed. Then he said something that troubled me. He told me he was totally taken aback by an interview in your office during which you showed him a letter from a captain he'd flown with — it was about a discussion that seems to have been blown up out of all proportion. He also said you had issued him with a warning. I can't find any note to that effect in the file, and neither can I find the letter. Were you a bit fierce with him?'

'Not particularly. I gave him a good talking to — he needed it — and said it was an informal warning, but if there was ever a next time, it would be formal, possibly leading to disciplinary action.'

'You really should note these things down, you know.'

'I didn't want to. Basically, he's a good lad, just needed a wake-up call and to stop preaching to his fellow crew members while in the air.' Ramsey went on to explain the background and why he had interviewed him. 'I destroyed the letter because I didn't want there to be a black mark in his file.'

'He also said you lectured him about his flying record.'

'Yes, I did — not his flying so much, as his poor technical knowledge, it seemed to have coincided with his new-found religious fervour. Seems he took his eye off the ball, so to speak.'

'It might help if you knew some of the things he discussed with me,' Sheila countered. 'You men don't always see so far beyond your noses; I think he found it easier to open up to a woman. He told me he was recently married, his new wife was also religious, they were both Baptists, that's how they'd met. She was very keen for him to do something really useful with his life rather than merely being an aerial bus driver, she had kept pressing him to make a change. Keith said he was very unhappy with some of his colleagues, they seemed to be more interested in chasing girls and drinking too much. You really should do something about that,' Sheila told Ramsey severely.

The turning point had come when he listened

to a Ugandan pastor talking about his work in Africa to help the poor, to heal the sick, to condemn the sin, but love the sinner. So many people needed guidance towards a better way of life. He described the good work being done by MAF to spread the love of Christ. From that moment, Keith knew exactly what he wanted to do, he could escape the sinful ways of his colleagues and be true to his God. 'The final spur was that interview with you. I think he'd been worrying for a long time. He liked flying, he said, but not with some of the colleagues he had to fly with.'

'In that case,' Ramsey replied, feeling a little chastened 'I'm sure Chalmers will be much happier working with people who share his values. I'll write a reference, saying that he is a man of integrity, has a good flying record — I won't mention the bit about him being distracted by his religious studies — and that I think he will be well suited to their work. I'll also telephone him to wish him well in his new career and, perhaps, advise him to discuss his faith a little more gently — he needs to encourage people rather than lecture them.'

Ramsey neither heard nor saw anything more of Chalmers, until some ten years later, at an aviation conference, when he picked up a copy of Flight Watch, the MAF magazine which lay amongst a pile of promotional literature. During one of the presentations, when the speaker was being particularly boring, Ramsey began to flip through the magazine and was surprised to come across a picture of Keith Chalmers standing beside a Cessna Caravan aircraft. What had first caught his experienced aviator's eye was the muddy dirt runway, the encroaching jungle down each side and the rugged hills at the far end. Judging by the low rain laden clouds he guessed the flying would have been far from easy.

Keith was wearing a pale blue shirt with captain's epaulets and a baseball cap with the MAF logo. He was surrounded by a group of colourfully clothed men and women waving palm fronds and who all appeared to be singing or cheering. The accompanying article described him as being one of their most experienced pilots, and gave an account of a typical day's work, flying out to remote villages in Rwanda, taking medical supplies and bringing sick people back to hospital in the main town. The photograph had been taken to

mark the arrival of two missionaries equipped with motorcycles so they could ride deep into the jungle to preach the gospel. It looked a very happy occasion.

There was a short interview with Keith in which he described how much he enjoyed the work. It was very humbling, he said, to take the word of Christ to such remote places and help save lives as well as souls.

Ramsey was delighted that Keith had found his true vocation.

In the Dark of the Night

L ook, I'll show you.' Ernie Colville turned down the cockpit lights, switched off the white ones, leaving only the reds. 'We'll need to wait a while, about twenty minutes for our eyes to adapt. You'll be surprised how much you can see, even when there's no moon.'

Gradually, as our night vision improved, he dimmed the red instrument lights still further. 'There — that's about it. Take a look out your side. Should be able to see the wing tip. I can see mine.' And indeed, I could. Even in the dark of the night, the horizon stood out as a clear straight line, the stars and the Milky Way unbelievably bright and the cloud layer beneath glowing in the starlight. 'Of course, if there's a moon, it feels like daylight.'

'Could you see other aircraft by starlight?'

'Only if they were really close, or silhouetted against the stars, or the lights on the ground. We didn't like the moon — it certainly helped us find the target, but it also helped the night fighters find us.'

Ernie was a quiet thoughtful man of around

forty-five, a cautious aviator, understanding and helpful to a young man like me, someone who encouraged you to do well. Below his BOAC wings, he wore a row of medal ribbons, amongst which I had noticed the diagonal purple and white stripes of the DFC — and the little silver rosette, showing he'd won it twice. His mild manner, slight build and sensitive face belied the raw courage he must have displayed over twenty years before.

I had flown with him several times. He never talked about what he'd done in the war, but I knew from his colleagues he'd flown Lancasters and Mosquitoes. At that time, I hadn't appreciated the significance of the small gold eagle he wore beneath his ribbons, it was only later, when I read about the Pathfinders, that I realised he had been one of that elite group. And what it meant.

It must have been in 1967 when I asked him how much he'd been able to see at night when on ops. I knew most of the ex-bomber pilots didn't like to be reminded of those days, and Ernie seemed particularly reticent — vulnerable even, an odd thing to say about a man like him. We were on our way back across the North Atlantic from Montreal when I posed the question. He took his time and replied, 'Look, I'll show you,' before turning down the lights. Then, when I insensitively asked him if he'd ever been frightened, he answered, 'Yes, we all were.' Long pause. 'Frequently.' And he immediately changed the subject.

I flew with him again around a year later, this time on a long trip out to Sydney and back via New York, Los Angeles, Honolulu and Fiji. On our way out to Australia, he said nothing about his wartime experiences and neither did I ask. It was not until our return journey across the Pacific when we reached Honolulu that he opened up a little, prompted, I'm sure, by the visit we had made to Pearl Harbour. By that time, we had spent nearly ten days together — perhaps it was the length of the trip, or he was in a reflective mood, or he knew I was a good listener, but gradually his story came out, not as a piece and nor did he tell it chronologically. I am sure, too, there were many gaps. For him, even though it was all in the past, I could see it was deeply etched in his mind. For me, as I write this fifty years later, my memory falters and some of the detail is lost, but what he said impressed me greatly. And it still does.

We were staying in the Reef Hotel on Waikiki beach. It was a popular honeymoon spot with many young couples wandering dreamily around with the stars in their eyes and sand on their toes. But for us, it was merely a good place to relax after the seven-hour flight across the water from Fiji, still trying to catch up with the jet lag. It was around here, on the way home, that one caught up with one's 'tummy time', still lagging behind on its way out towards Australia.

Earlier in the day, we had been to the USS Arizona memorial, a white bridge-like structure spanning the ship's hull which lay exactly where she had come to rest after being sunk by Japanese bombs. It was a sobering experience to look down into the water at the ship, clearly visible beneath the surface, knowing it was a war grave with the bodies of so many young sailors still trapped inside. Only the rusted circular barbette of the number three turret remained above the water. Ernie had been unusually quiet as we gazed down, even more so when we read the names on the marble slab commemorating all those who had died on that 'day of infamy' in December 1941. He'd also remained very quiet when we returned to the hotel. The rest of the crew were nowhere around, we found out later they'd all gone to Trader Vic's Polynesian restaurant and bar — a raucous place with girls in grass skirts serving rum punches and other strong liquor. Ernie was in a contemplative mood and, wanting a peaceful place to muse on what we had seen, he suggested we go to the coffee shop in the hotel for a hamburger and then up to his room for a beer.

Near the end of our meal, he said, 'I remember Pearl Harbour so well. I was still in the middle of my training — flying Oxfords. When we heard the news, all we thought was, 'Thank God, we're no longer alone.' Seeing the Arizona brought it all back. Over a thousand dead on that one ship and our only thoughts that day being ones of relief. It's ironic to think we were so pleased.'

IN THE DARK OF THE NIGHT

We called for the check and paid the waitress, 'You guys have a nice day now.' Funny thing to say so late in the evening, I thought.

'Let's go up and order some beers from room service.' Ernie's balcony looked out over Waikiki beach. We sat in the dark looking out to sea, the lights of some ships moving slowly out towards the horizon, waves swishing dreamily on the sand below, a girl's laughter drifting up to us where we sat high up on the seventh floor, and the muted hum of traffic far away. Such a peaceful scene. 'Do you remember that time when you asked me how much we could see at night? Over the Atlantic, flying home to London.'

I said I did. 'You were surprised, weren't you?' I agreed.

And he started to tell me a little about himself. He'd been educated at a minor public school in Walsall and was expected to follow in his father's footsteps as an accountant. He was 17 when war came, still at school, playing soldiers in the OTC, but he had no wish to be a soldier. Straight from school, he signed up to join the RAF. He'd been kept waiting around for a few months before the call came to present himself at Babbacombe, near Torquay in south Devon. There they were issued with uniforms and kit, taught basic drill, inoculated for overseas service, taken on long route marches, and given lectures on service life. Next, when they started their initial training, his barracks was the Majestic Hotel

157

in Torquay, not as grand as it sounded; it was requisitioned and had obviously seen better days. He remembered long hours of ground school learning about engines, navigation, electrical systems, instruments, Morse code, and aerodynamics. They didn't see an aircraft for eight weeks. When he passed out, he was promoted to Leading Aircraftman and issued with a white 'flash' to be worn in his forage cap — now at last everyone could see he was a real trainee airman.

He was given some leave and posted to the Brooklands Flying Club at Fairoaks, where he learnt to fly on Tiger Moths. And what a contrast that proved to be! It was also the home of two other flying clubs. The Chief Flying Instructor was an RAF Squadron Leader, the instructors a mix of service and civilian pilots. Discipline was lax and he was billeted in a local hotel. He remembered two months of glorious summer and the new-found thrill of flying, the best time he'd ever had in the RAF, he said. Next it was 'down to earth' again and the hard reality of winter at Lyneham doing his twin rating on Oxfords, the 'Ox Box' he called it. 'Not a bad little aeroplane, good for cross country navigation training and night flying.' But it had been hard work learning instrument flying, navigation and coping with the bad weather. And that was where, part way through his course, he had heard about the attack on Pearl Harbour.

In February '42 he was posted to Abingdon for his operational training on Whitleys.

'Horrible bloody things, leaked like sieves.' Life improved when he was transferred to Wellingtons, 'Much nicer to fly, though they were all pretty well clapped-out.'

Suddenly he stopped and stared out to sea with faraway eyes. He remained silent for a long time. Then he started as though from a trance, took a swig of his beer and said, 'I'll tell you about my first operational trip, it was that thousand bomber raid. The one on Cologne. Harris dragged out every aircraft he could find, including those of us still in training. I went with my instructor in a Wellington, it could carry two pilots, neither of us wanted to go, but orders are orders.' He stopped again. 'Such a clear moonlit night — much brighter than anything I showed you. We were in a huge stream of aircraft, I could see everything; the ones close on either side, even those above and ahead of us.'

He said they were below the Lancs and the other four-engine heavies. It had all felt so unreal, it was as though he was suspended motionless in space. 'We could see for miles.' At first, the moonlight reflecting off the sea and then, over the land, sudden gleams flashing off lakes and rivers as they passed. There had been no opposition until, far ahead, he began to see the orange glow of the fires in Cologne, search lights probing the sky, and strings of orange beads climbing slowly into the sky.

'I didn't know what to expect. Then it really hotted up.' He described the menacing red bursts of flak around them and overhead, the smell of cordite as they passed through the bursts ahead — and the ocean of flames beneath.' With that, he stopped and stared again out to sea. 'It was horrible and it was beautiful.'

I said I'd seen some genuine wartime colour footage that looked pretty impressive. He said that wasn't reality. Nothing could show what it was really like. But they had got back alright — not a scratch on his aircraft. Ernie's whole demeanour had changed. Until that point, I guessed flying had been fun — from now on it would be very different. Again, he was silent. I decided to break the spell, 'When was that?' I asked gently.

'May '42.' He continued to sit silently sipping his beer with that same faraway look in his eyes. 'A little later, in June, after I'd finished my training, I joined my first operational squadron at Helmsbury, north of Lincoln. Small place, you won't have heard of it. Initially we had Wellingtons but then the whole squadron was re-equipped with Lancs — so much better than the old Wimpy. On my twenty-first raid, we were hit by flak over Holland. Only just made it back. One engine out, leaking fuel all over the place.

'Managed to land at Beccles. It's just inland from Lowestoft. First place we saw as we crossed the coast. Still being built, not finished. We were low down. I was running out of strength. But at least it had a runway

— almost dead ahead. Seemed like a miracle. I'd been shot up with some shrapnel in my left leg and went to hospital for a while. I guess that saved my life. Most of my friends — the ones I joined up with — never survived the war.'

I had noticed his slight limp and asked if he'd found it difficult to hold on full rudder. 'A bit. I think that's why they sent me instructing on Lancs, my leg was good for that, even with an engine out. It's OK now.' He smiled a little ruefully, 'But I'm glad I'm on VC10s, not 707s.'

Then he had a stroke of luck and managed to wangle a posting to 627 Squadron at Oakington, flying Mosquitoes. 'That suited me very well, no more area bombing, all low-level precision strikes and, later, marking targets for the heavies. And one of the best aircraft — ever.' He was happy doing that because they were hitting military and strategic targets rather than blanket bombing cities. He continued with that until the end of the war. 'Two strokes of luck — being injured and then flying Mossies.'

I asked how he came to fetch up in BOAC. 'Joined BSAA in '45, Don Bennett's out-fit. We flew Lancastrians at first, much the same as a Lancaster, but not much good for passengers. When BSAA folded we became part of BOAC. That's why I'm here today. And now I think it's time for bed.' We exchanged a few more trifles and wished each other goodnight.

Next day, we flew to Los Angeles as though the conversation had never happened. Nothing more was said, either there or during our next stop in New York, or on the last leg across the Atlantic to London.

I didn't see him again until about eighteen months later on a trip to Hong Kong and back. It was October. On the way home, we flew into the Seychelles from Colombo, arriving in a thunderstorm amidst gusty winds and torrents of rain. It was touch and go as to whether we would make it in. The rain was so heavy, it was barely possible to see the lighthouse and eyeball our way along the coast towards the airfield. And it continued to rain for the whole three days we were there. There was nothing to do other than sit around and read books.

On the second day, as the rain poured down, we propped up the bar and watched the wind blowing chairs and sunshades into the hotel swimming pool. 'That's the third parasol I've seen take off today. Can't be much fun when you've paid good money for a holiday on a tropical island. Lying brochures don't say there's not much sun and it rains like hell,' I remarked to Ernie.

'I don't think they'll mind, most of them are honeymooners. They'll be alright canoodling in bed. Not so bad on a honeymoon, eh?' was all he replied.

Later that evening after the thunderstorms had passed, we sat outside in the soft cool air of the evening. The sky had cleared, the stars were bright, and a half-moon was creeping slowly up from the eastern horizon, shedding its light across the sea towards us. The others on the crew had long gone to bed, leaving the two of us to finish the remains of Ernie's scotch; it was an ideal time for reminiscing. We sipped our drinks beneath the gentle rustle of the coconut palms. 'It's good to have peaceful evenings like this sometimes. Even the rain feels better in the tropics. Do you remember that evening in Honolulu?'

'Yes, you were telling me about your time in the RAF. Somewhere in Lincolnshire, you'd just moved on to Mosquitoes.'

'I was so lucky to get on Mossies. Not like that first raid over Cologne. Looking back on it now, it all seems so weird. Nights of sheer terror followed by the peace and quiet of the English countryside. I remember lying on my back on the grass, listening to larks singing above the airfield, walking along canal banks, watching ducks with my girlfriend, evenings in the village pub — and then, having to face another of those ghastly nights yet again. It went on and on and on 'till you didn't come back. Lost most of my friends. I wonder now why we did it.' He poured himself another whisky. 'We were all so young. But, at the time, we knew exactly why we were doing it — to hit Hitler hard. I've never had anything against the German people, not even then. But war is war, you have to wage it by all means possible. That hideous gang of Nazis had to be defeated, I'm even more sure of it now.' A long pause. 'I don't hold with all the revisionist stuff you hear from armchair critics spouting on the telly — they weren't there, they never knew what it was like. They go on about how we weren't able to hit anything — they've no idea how hard it was.'

Once again, that faraway look I'd seen before came into his eyes. Suddenly, he turned and dabbed at the corner of an eye. I think he hoped I hadn't seen, because he quickly stood up and went into his room to fetch a bottle of soda from the fridge — at least, that's what he said he was doing. I sat silently, not wanting to break his mood.

'Mossies were so much better, we actually managed to hit the right targets,' he laughed. 'And we were fast enough or high enough to avoid the fighters.'

I topped up his glass. 'But what was so special about Cologne?'

I poured myself another whisky while I waited for him to answer.

'First op, I suppose.' Then a long sigh, 'I haven't told many people this before. My mother was German, my first name is Ernst. Called myself Ernest when I joined up, didn't want anyone to know.'

I watched as he fiddled with his glass. 'My father is Scottish, from Ayrshire, not far from Prestwick airport in fact. After the first war he was in Germany for a while, in Cologne, not sure why, but he met a girl, they got married and he brought his new wife back to live in England. The rest is history, as they say. I was born in 1922, my brother three years later. He was killed in '44, only nineteen years old. Such a waste.'

He stopped, took some more sips of his whisky. I waited for him to continue. 'After it was all over, the war that is, and I'd been demobbed, I went to Cologne in late '45. I wanted to see if I could find my mother's family. She'd heard nothing from them since summer '39. No answers to any of her letters. She was desperate to know what'd happened to her sister. All gone — except for the son — my young cousin. He would have been only ten years old when we bombed the place, but somehow he'd survived. I remember it like yesterday. The damage was simply appalling. Mile after mile of ruins, no roofs, only the shells of buildings and piles of rubble. I couldn't believe the mess, and even then you felt you could smell death. I found him eventually, living with some relatives in Ostheim, a small town to the south of the city.

'Didn't tell him I'd been in the Air Force. And I never told my family I'd been over Cologne. Never talked about it, didn't want to upset them. He seemed happy enough with the relatives. But they didn't have much to eat. When I reported all this back to my mother, she arranged to send food parcels. She wrote to the boy regularly, but she never plucked up the courage to go back to Cologne.' Ernie surreptitiously rubbed his eye again. 'I saw Heini, that's short for Heinrich, again much later — that would've been in '59, in England. He was a young man of twenty-six by then and doing well, he came over to do a post grad in classical archaeology at Merton College. His first degree was in classical history at Heidelberg, Roman archaeology was his thing. By then, I was flying for BOAC and we were living near Oxford. Naturally he wanted to meet his aunt, my mother, so we had him to stay. I liked him immediately, I speak German fairly well; I like the people and their culture. Now he knew I'd been in the RAF but was kind enough to joke that the only good thing about the war was finding so many Roman remains which we had helped uncover by all that bombing. That was why he'd become so interested in archaeology. I said I'd love to come and see them sometime.'

After dinner, he and Heini had stayed up talking about the past, antiquities had featured a lot in their conversation but, towards the end of the evening, Heini began to describe how dreadful it had been on the receiving end of the bombing. Ernie thought Heini had wanted to rub it in a bit. He couldn't blame him really. He wasn't bitter, he just wanted to talk about what it felt like to live in a cellar with the house above their heads being rocked by bombs, wondering if he'd be buried alive, walking through rubble smelling of death and destruction, going to school in a partly bombed-out ruin, and lying awake at night waiting for the next time. His parents and grandmother had been killed in the big raid of May '42, but he'd survived and been taken in by some neighbours. When they were bombed out too, later that same year, he'd been dragged from the rubble and left to wander the streets alone until some friends of the family rescued him and took him to Ostheim.

'I didn't tell him I'd been in the thousand bomber raid that killed his family. I muttered something about mainly targeting coastal facilities, U-boat pens and things like that, which was only partly true. He could see I was very uncomfortable, he left off after that. You see, his grandmother was also my grandmother, and his mother was my aunt. Was it me who killed them? I felt so bad. I still feel it now. We knew Hitler was pure evil. We knew it had to be done, but Bomber Command was the only way we could take the war to him. It was a blunt weapon, but it was the only one we had. We had to do it. I have no regrets about that part of it, but it doesn't stop me feeling guilty for having bombed my own family.'

We both sat quietly lost in our own thoughts. So many families on all sides had suffered during two World Wars. I knew mine had, and so many more too, throughout Europe and across the world. And for what? It all seemed so needless, but it was a necessary evil. There was no doubt the Nazis had to be stopped. Ernie must have been thinking similar thoughts. Suddenly he looked up and remarked, 'The irony is that my mother's family were all Catholics, totally anti-Hitler and all he stood for, if they could have got rid of him, they would've.'

Dinner in Moscow

Moscow 1997. At last, our difficult two-day meeting with the Federal Aviation Authority of Russia (FAAR) is over. Yet we know it will not be the last if we are to persuade the Russians to open new shorter routes over northern Siberia between Europe and Japan. We also want to use them flexibly to take best advantage of the jet stream as it varies from day to day, but it seems 'flexibility' is not a word to be found in the Russian negotiators' phrasebook. However, now that we have left the meeting room, their stony-faced and immovable attitude quickly melts away and a more warm hearted and humorous camaraderie emerges.

So here we are in a magnificent dining room. Two large tables dominate the room, one is covered with canapés of various sorts — zakuski, our hosts informs us — caviar blinis, morsels of smoked fish, salamis and pickles, the other is laid for our formal dinner. I am impressed by the opulence, the oriental rugs on the floor, regally patterned wall papers, decorative plasterwork on the ceiling, heavy velvet curtains, magnificent chandeliers, and ornate sconces on the walls.

'Do you know where we are?' our host inquires. I tell him, no. 'This was Stalin's dining room,' he says proudly, then, drawing back the curtains, he opens the French windows and gestures theatrically towards the opening. 'And this was private box overlooking racecourse.'

Waiters start serving champagne from the Crimea. 'Sovetskoye Shampanskoye, is good?' I agree, even though it is a little sweet. After some small talk, we are invited to try the zakuski, it is delicious. 'And now we drink vodka.' The waiters fill small shot glasses for each of us. 'I show you, breath out, drink, eat — you must eat.' Our host exhales, throws back the shot in one and then bites into a large pickle. 'Important you eat. For head.' He points to his temple and rolls his eyes.

'Now we toast.' He pauses until all our glasses have been refilled. 'I drink to success of our negotiations.'

I reply, 'I drink to Mother Russia, may we fly over her beautiful land in peace.' Others follow, some in Russian which I do not understand. Our host is right, it is essential to eat after each shot of vodka.

We take our places, formally seated alternately between our Russian counterparts. We are served a clear consommé. Next comes salmon in pastry, koulibiak — delicious when accompanied by more Crimean champagne. This is followed by Beef Stroganov and a robust Georgian red wine.

Finally, the dessert, a rich concoction of honey and cream, served in the Russian fashion accompanied by black tea. By this time the gathering is becoming distinctly merry, jokes are flying around the table in a mixture of Russian and English.

Then it is time for speeches. Our host begins with a formal speech in Russian through our interpreter who, fortunately, has kept a clear head. It is a serious speech; I am not sure quite how to take it. He talks about the rights of access to the new routes we are proposing, the difficulty of finding and training enough English-speaking air traffic controllers, how all this will need money and time, he is looking forward to our help.

Oh dear, I know where this is leading: it is a veiled hint about the need for extra payments from the airlines over and above the normal charges for navigation services, something which is against the ICAO convention. Our delegate from Cathay Pacific signals that he would like to speak next. He stands and warmly applauds the FAAR for being so open to the idea of new north/south routes over the North Pole between Hong Kong and the USA. He looks forward to these being both profitable for the airlines and a fresh source of revenue for the Russians, another not-so-veiled hint about more money for the administration.

Then it is my turn. I feel the evening is becoming far too serious. When I rise, I begin by thanking our host for giving us such a delicious dinner and for doing so in such prestigious surroundings. I propose a toast of thanks to him and to the FAAR for engaging in these promising negotiations. When everyone has drained their glass, I glance at the ceiling for inspiration and say that I am reminded of something. With their permission, I would like to recount an amusing story rather than make a formal speech. Heads nod around the table, people relax, push their chairs back and signal for more wine.

'May I ask you to cast your minds back to the 1970s, Alexei Kosygin was in power, Russia was a very different place, and I was flying Boeing 707s through Moscow to Tokyo. At Sheremetyevo airport, the border guards carefully examined our passports with all the diligence you would expect. On our way into town, I remember being surprised when we passed the Ezhi Memorial. I had never realised how close the Nazi armies had come to Moscow before being turned back in December 1941 during the Great Patriotic War. I salute the bravery of the Russian people, so few of us in the rest of Europe know how close they came.' There is a murmur of appreciation around the table.

'Unlike today, the streets were nearly empty — very few people, only a few cars, and some buses and lorries. We arrived at the Ukraina

Hotel, that grand Stalinist building, looking like a wedding cake, with an enormously tall spire surmounted by a red Hammer and Sickle.' I speak slowly so the interpreter can relay the story. My audience is puzzled, some look a little displeased. 'Please forgive me for reminding you of those days. But it may amuse you to know that at that time, we BOAC pilots referred to our headquarters building at Heathrow as 'The Kremlin'. We used to make rude remarks about the managers who inhabited it, and the strange edicts that emanated from it. Perhaps some of you may have felt the same about your Kremlin.' I see several Russian heads nod and a few wry smiles. I begin to feel a little better about telling my story.

'When we first started flying to Moscow, the flight manager, in his infinite wisdom, decided to issue a Flight Crew Notice. It said, 'We are aware that many of you refer to our headquarters as 'The Kremlin'. It is most probable that your hotel rooms in Moscow will be bugged. Therefore, you are recommended to refrain from making derogatory remarks about the Kremlin for fear that they are misinterpreted with unfortunate consequences.' Of course everyone treated this as a huge joke.' Russian faces are breaking into broad grins, I think I am on a winner.

'As you may know, the Ukraina had a vast foyer, I guess it still does. Opposite the main entrance doors was a long reception desk. We presented the crew list and were each given a piece of paper which we were told to exchange for our room keys. We ascended in the lifts, wonderful old-fashioned lifts with metal grills and wooden panelling. But they were rather wobbly.' I use my hands to illustrate an exceedingly wobbly ascent.

'When I emerged from the lift, I found myself in a long corridor with doors down one side. At the far end of the corridor, behind a table, there sat a grim looking 'Dragon Lady', dressed all in black. She was as broad as she was tall.' I hold my arms out to indicate her circumference and then fold them, trying to look like Grandma in those old Giles cartoons. At this, my audience starts to chuckle.

'I tried my very few words of Russian — dobroye utra, pozhaluysta and spasiba — but she was not impressed. Perhaps it was my appalling accent. I exchanged my piece of paper for the room key, and she shooed me away.' More chuckles at my attempts to speak Russian.

'Captains were given grand spacious suites — a large sitting room with sofas and chairs, a bedroom with a huge double bed, and a bathroom. But there was one problem.' I pause. 'When I went into the bathroom — *Quelle horreur!* — no bath plugs, no soap, no toilet paper and towels that felt like sandpaper.' I grimace and throw my hands in the air in mock despair. Now they are really laughing, it is going down alright, they are on my side.

'It was always our custom after a flight for the whole crew to gather in the captain's room for a party. Extra sandwiches were provided by BOAC for us to take off the aircraft, to which we added cans of beer, and some bottles of champagne and wine. Soon, the party was going well and the chief steward, who was a good raconteur, told a story of what had happened on a previous stay in Moscow. And it is his story which I will now relate. The captain had suggested, he said, they should all search for the hidden bugs. 'What a good idea,' everyone thought, and the flight engineer was sent to collect his tools. All good flight engineers carry a number of small tools in their briefcases so they can do minor repairs on the aircraft — spanners, screwdrivers and such like. It is not for nothing that are they called 'flying spanners". The interpreter seems to be having difficulty translating this last remark.

'You can imagine what happened next. People looked behind pictures, felt the walls for bumps and hidden wires, the engineer dismantled the telephones, each part was examined, light fittings were unscrewed and put back together again, the bed was moved, the mattress and pillows examined, the underneath of tables closely inspected, wardrobes moved away from the walls, cushions lifted from the sofas and chairs, and door frames felt for strange appliances.' I mime the search in an exaggerated fashion and am rewarded with much hilarity. I ask for some water and drink while the laughter subsides.

'But nothing was found.'

I scratch my head and put on a puzzled look. Then I point beneath the dining table. ''Look,' says the captain, 'there is a lump under the carpet.' They moved the table away from between the sofas, the carpet was rolled back and, there, for all to see, was a mysterious metallic object. The flight engineer was asked to use his biggest spanner. He began to unscrew the device. Suddenly, there was a graunching noise.' I illustrate the point by making appropriate noises. 'The centre of the device disappeared followed by a loud crash and the sound of tinkling glass.' I pause, then look up at the ceiling to where there is a huge chandelier hanging over Stalin's dining table. My audience looks too and roars with laughter. I wait, timing is all.

'Of course, the crew were astonished. What could have happened? Horrified, they replaced the device on the floor to exactly where it had been before the accident. They rolled back the carpet and returned the table to its original position, then continued the party as though nothing had happened.

'Half an hour later, there was loud knocking on the door. A worried looking hotel manager came in with some workmen and asked to inspect the fitting under the table. 'It is chandelier,' he said. The captain decided to bluff it out. Keeping a straight face, he quietly pointed out that some of the others may be unsafe too and demanded they check the fittings in the room above. He was sure the manager did not want another accident. What would BOAC have to say if their crews were injured and they had to cancel flights to Tokyo and even worse, maybe, the contract with the hotel? Should he report it to the Kremlin? He asked.'

By this time my audience is beside themselves with mirth. The evening has been a great success. Next day, our Russian friends are still chuckling, and we end on a happy note.

Sometimes jokes can work wonders. Ever after, whenever I visited Moscow for discussions with the FAAR, I was greeted with big smiles and digs about dodgy chandeliers.

They never tired of hearing my story again.

The Bombshell on the Beach

T hree times, three times,' he muttered. 'Three bloody times, I've been locked out of my own house by an angry woman.' And he shouted obscenities into the sky. Terry knew she was in there. He tried the locks, found the door bolted, banged on it, went round the house, rattled the jalousies, tried at the back — no answer. He thought about breaking in but gave up and walked down to the old lean-to behind the hangars on the south side of the runway at Vigie. It was comfortable enough, with a couple of chairs, an old settee, a fridge and a gas ring on which he often cooked snacks while working on the aircraft.

He found some beer, shouted more obscenities into the night and gazed morosely out to sea at the last of the tropical sunset. He decided to sleep there and go back to the house in the morning after she had left for work.

He dozed, dreamt and woke in a bad mood. The sun was up, he made some coffee, searched for something to eat, but found nothing. He contemplated his next move. The house was his, but when Angélique came to live with him, she had made changes; too many in his view, and not always for the better. It was a small house, much smaller than she would have liked, but it suited him. It was close to his work, not far from the beach and near Castries, the main town where she owned a shop selling expensive knick-knacks to tourists.

When he returned, he found all the doors wide open — even the bug screens — and no Angie, no car and none of her things. He was relieved that some of her clutter had gone too. No doubt she would be telling her many friends and relatives in Castries about the row, and they would be taking her side. He thought back to the other times this had happened, what was it that caused his women to take against him so?

Thank God he and Angie were not married, only living together, it would be cheaper this time. He remembered when his first wife locked him out after that hilarious trip to Hong Kong, and told him not to come back. The divorce was acrimonious and outrageously expensive. He managed to find a small bachelor pad in Richmond and persuade Amanda to join him, but she was far too conventional for that sort of arrangement and soon went off to marry one of her horsey friends. He drifted, consoled by various girlfriends, and enjoyed himself down the routes.

When he married again, the second Mrs Flynn, who was eight years younger than him, wanted a decent house and garden in which to bring up the new baby. They settled into respectable domestic life in a small village near Reading — that was until Juanita arrived from Peru, claiming she was preggers and he was the prospective father. The second Mrs Flynn knew he had been a bit of a lad but thought she had reformed him. Finding Juanita on the doorstep was too much, she promptly left. This time the alimony had not only to support both mother and daughter, but Juanita's little boy as well. Her generalissimo had kicked her out when he found she was pregnant by another man. Terry, even on his 747 captain's salary, found himself very hard up. Neither his colleagues nor his flight manager had the least sympathy.

When he reached retirement age, he decided to make a complete break, leave England and go out to the Caribbean. He had seen an ad in *Flight* Magazine from a small air taxi outfit, based in St Lucia, wanting an experienced pilot to fly twin engine Beech Barons between the islands. He needed the money, living expenses were cheap, and he fancied the idea of a care-free life in the sun. For five years it had suited him well. The flying was fun, the weather good, the clientele a mixed bunch — mainly tourists sightseeing or wanting to connect with the other islands and business people who found it quicker and more convenient to fly direct rather than through the main airports. The routes ranged as far north as Jamaica and south down to Trinidad. The boss was fair, the hours reasonable, flying mostly by day, and his colleagues were friendly. There were four pilots, three aircraft, one mechanic and a secretary who did all the admin.

Vigie airport, more formally known as the George F L Charles Airport, has a short east/west runway lying parallel to the beach close to Castries. The terminal, such as it is, is on the north side where the beach turns towards the peninsula. On the southern side lies the town of Sansouci and Point Seraphine where the cruise ships tie up. It was an easy walk, from Sansouci where Terry lived, past the football ground and down Seraphine Road to the hangers.

Angie had come into his life when he flew her down to Grenada and later to Montserrat where her father had business interests in the small town of Brades. They flew up the western side of the island, keeping well clear of the recent volcanic activity and landed at the little hump-backed airport in the north. The family house was unoccupied, they stayed overnight and the inevitable happened. Back in Castries, they became an item and Angie moved in. Her father's family were of Irish descent and, being Catholic, disapproved. Her mother from Jamaica was more forgiving. This exotic cultural and ethnic mix was striking, and Terry was easily struck.

◊◊◊

The first disaster came when his boss was accused of drug running. Terry had harboured suspicions. It worried him, but having no proof, he had turned a blind eye and kept well clear. When the authorities decided to investigate, they shut down the air taxi business, leaving Terry and the other employees to live off their savings. The resulting belt-tightening did not please Angélique one bit, it was not what she had expected.

The seeds for the second disaster were sown on the day before the row. Terry was walking down Bridge Street on his way to the Scotiabank when he heard a sudden shout of, 'Taff!' No one had called him Taff since he'd retired, he turned and there was Jim Ford, an old colleague from British Airways.

'Taff, what the devil are you doing here? Join me for a beer? There's a bar just round the corner.' Terry explained he couldn't stop; he had an appointment with his bank manager. 'How about lunch tomorrow? Sophie and I are staying at The Rendezvous. Why don't you join us? Bring your current girl. Bet you have one. Twelve o'clock, OK?'

Reluctantly, Terry agreed. He wasn't too sure about discussing old times, nor about taking Angie. He wondered what Jim might reveal. That evening, he told her about Jim, mentioned the invitation, but secretly hoped she would decline because of the shop. Surprisingly, she said her assistant could easily cope for the afternoon, she'd never been to The Rendezvous and, if Jim was paying, she'd like to come. 'I'll be there at twelve.'

Terry arrived promptly at midday. Jim and Sophie were waiting in the open-air bar near the beach enjoying a rum punch. They waved him over, 'Don't think you've met Sophie, have you? Sophie, this is Taff, I'm sure I've told you about him.'

Sophie smiled, she'd been a stewardess before marrying Jim and recognised Taff instantly. But it seemed he did not remember her, should she say anything?

'Rum punch? We've already started.' Jim went on, 'And I could certainly do with another.'

Sophie sipped her drink, 'Cheers Taff. Has the penny dropped? VC10s, African routes, fun in the Far East?' And to jog his memory, 'Sophie Baldwin — Nairobi.'

And Taff remembered, the hangar doors began to open, all the old stories tumbling out. He relaxed, so like the old days, he thought. 'It was fun then, wasn't it?'

Another round of rum punches oiled the proceedings — do you remember Chris trying to feed an elephant up the wrong end? Bugger turned round and gave him a trunkful. And Charlie Squires landing at the wrong airport in The Gulf? No one knew until two sets of landing fees arrived on the flight manager's desk — Stuffie Sanders, remember him? And what about Vernon Blades being rostered with Ron Gillette? And Dave Price jumping on his fruit basket. Then the roster clerk who managed to crew a whole aircraft with Smiths, caused merry hell in Delhi, customs bloke wouldn't accept the crew declaration, thought they were taking the piss. What about that girl with the pink E-Type, wonder what happened to her? And, of course, your honeymoon in Hong Kong......

◊◊◊

'Good Lard have mercy 'pon me, look at de time! Zina, shut up shop fi me? Need be at de Rendezvous at twelve.' Angélique found a mirror, applied some lipstick, tidied her hair, grabbed her handbag and rushed out. Why American tourists take so long? Why can't they make their mind up quick? Bloody cruise ships, good for business, but what a pain.

The Vide Bouteille Road was crowded with lunchtime traffic, and she was late, what would Terry say? Him always so damn punctual. Come on, come on. Shute! Dat a close one. Look where you're fuckin' goin'. Calm down, girl. Rendezvous Beach swish place an' Terry wan' me look good. Woops, where dat one come from? She swung round the roundabout into the drive and found a parking spot near the entrance. Easy now, girl, keep it cool. This place for romantic couples, me anything but romantic.

The two men were sitting at the bar with their backs toward her. Guess de fat one's Jim, but where his wife? Terry was telling jokes — blue ones she guessed, and Jim was laughing. Dey haven't seen me yet, hang back, not comfy with no other woman. Ah, dat Jim's wife? Coming back now? She tall, good looking — slim, fifty I tink, grey-blonde hair. Her look kind, make me feel better, never wanted to come really, but I tink I can face dem now.

'Angel babe.' How I hate dat. An' in front of all dem strangers too. She tried to smile as Terry gave her a peck on the cheek.

'Jim, this is Angélique.'

'Angie, Jim, an old flying mate from way back. And Sophie, his other half.'

'Can I get you a drink?' Jim asked, 'We're on rum punches.'

'Just a Red Stripe please, have to be back at work later.' By de look of him he have one too many, an' Sophie ain' happy. 'What was that about honeymoons in Hong Kong?'

'Nothing really. Taff here,' said Jim, looking pointedly at Terry. 'Got up to quite a lark. It was Bill Williams, wasn't it, who set you up with that Berkeley girl? You know the vicar's daughter. Ouch! what did you do that for?' And glared at his wife who had surreptitiously kicked him on the ankle.

'Shall we go and eat? I think Angie has to work this afternoon.' She gave Sophie a grateful look. She understand.

The men ordered more rum punches and they all went through to their table by the beach. Why Terry so different wid Jim here? Him coarser, louder; not de Terry I know. Make me feel uncomfy, I no longer hungry. 'Only a little salad please, no wine.'

Jim had definitely had too much wine, it didn't mix well with the rum. So, I tink, has Terry.

Glad I have to be back at shop soon, he have whole afternoon to sleep it off afore I get home.

Jim leant across to Terry and asked confidentially, 'You still married to that Nicola bird then Taff?'

Sophie was embarrassed, Terry looked sheepish, Angie was stunned. 'Is that true?

Dat why you no marry me?' Jim opened his mouth to say something but was shushed by Sophie. Terry made no reply.

'Answer me, will you. How many women you have? Me 'jus your new fancy girl den.' Angie threw her napkin on the table and jumped to her feet, shouting, 'Yu bloodclaat!'

Heads turned at the other tables. She stomped out onto the beach, 'You useless man, you tik me fi pretty dunce, you jus' gyalis, you tink you cocksman, but you only sof' man!'

Then she went back to the table, slapped Terry on the face, 'You hear me, you no jook wi' me agin.'

At that she grabbed her bag, marched out to her car, drove home in an evil temper, locked all the doors and collapsed on the bed. Much later, she was woken by Terry shouting and banging on the doors round the house. She ignored him. He never say 'till now him still married, an' I see him lookin' at girl in bar. How many women he still fucking? An' why he can't do it wi' me anymore. I never want see him again, he can go to hell on a broomstick.'

When night fell and all was quiet, she packed all the things she could fit into her little car and drove to the shop where she had a flat upstairs.

A couple of weeks later, on a dreary February day, Jim ducked under the doorway into the warmth of the Bell Inn in Wendham. After the Caribbean, he was feeling the cold.

'You bin away then? Somewhere 'ot was it?'

'St Lucia, on holiday.' As he watched Tom carefully pull three pints of Autumn Gold. 'Sun, sand, rum punches, that sort of thing. Not my cup of tea really, but Sophie likes it.'

'Better'n 'ere, then? Forecast says snow, won't be many in tonight.'

There were only five then — Tom behind the bar, old Bob on his usual stool, wet dog at his feet, and Keith and Alex warming their backsides in front of the fire, waiting for their beers.

'That'll be nine pound-sixty.'

Jim passed the money over and took the pints to the table by the fire. What a change of scene, he thought, last week tropical heat, today cold sleet in the English countryside. He liked this Chilterns pub, its low beams, the log fire, the friendly locals and the well-kept beer.

'Good holiday?' Keith asked.

'Yes, bloody sight better than all this rain, and Tom says it'll turn to snow later. Oh well — Moscow on Monday, so I suppose I'd better get used to it.'

They were old friends, flying for the same airline, living near each other and meeting up in The Bell from time to time. It had become a ritual to compare notes after their various trips to the far corners of the world. Jim was bursting to tell them his news.

'Bet you can't guess who I saw.'

'Go on.'

'Old Taff — Taff Flynn, remember him, always chasing the girls?'

'What, the one with three wives?'

'Yes, but not all at the same time.'

'What's he up to now?'

'Still flying — air taxi, sightseeing, that kind of stuff.'

'Expect he needs the money. All those women must have cost him a fortune in alimony. Never understood him.'

'Well, there's another one in tow now. Real stunner, young, dark skinned, come-to-bed eyes.'

'That doesn't surprise me. Married her has he?'

'No, and I don't expect he will. Not after what happened in St Lucia.' And he started to tell them the story. 'We were on holiday, Sophie and me, a romantic escape in the sun. I bumped into Taff in Castries, the main town, and invited him to lunch at our hotel. He came with his girl in tow. We had a few drinks, d'you know The Rendezous?'

'That swish place on the beach?' said Alex, 'Not my sort of place at all.'

Keith agreed, but it had suited Jim and Sophie. 'We had hardly sat down to eat when she started sounding off. Seems Taff had never told her he was still married. She was furious. Jumped up, sent glasses flying across the table, marched out onto the beach and started shouting at the top of her voice in Jamaican lingo. Hardly understood a word. But Taff did and so did the staff in the restaurant.'

'What did she say?' asked Keith.

'Called him a cocksman.'

'That sounds about right,' laughed Alex. 'Sums him up perfectly.'

'And that wasn't all, said he was a soft man.'

At which point Keith, spluttered into is beer, 'You know what that means?'

'No.'

'Means he can't get it up any more.'

'Poor old Taff,' added Alex, 'What a terrible end.'

'Couldn't happen to a better chap!'

The Undertaker's Wind

I f you walk up Third Avenue to 55th you will see a low brick building incongruously surrounded by skyscrapers. This is P J Clarke's. In the early '60s, it was one of my favourite New York restaurants. Back then, it served excellent oysters, burgers, steaks and an especially good beer beef stew, I guess it still does. Being Irish, their cool creamy Guinness on tap was the best in town.

The three of us, Alan Gardner, our young second officer; Len Crabtree, the flight engineer and I had flown in from London that afternoon and, as we were due to go on down to Jamaica the following evening, we decided to meet up here for an early dinner. We ordered our Guinness, sat at the bar and waited for our captain, Harry Stoneham, to join us. In those days, BOAC captains stayed in superior hotels while the rest of us stayed in the Lexington.

'Well, what do you think?' I asked as Alan looked round at the old-fashioned brick and wood panelled interior, red and white gingham tablecloths, bentwood chairs, faded photos of film stars and sportsmen covering the walls, and — the vast array of drinks behind the bar. 'Even stayed open during prohibition, so they say.'

'Oldest bar in Manhattan,' added Len, 'Been here since eighteen something or other.'

But Alan, remembering our arrival into JFK, was still on a high. The flight over had been routine, Harry flying, me navigating across the pond, and Alan in the co-pilot's seat so he could experience North Atlantic HF radio procedures — and American ATC, which is something else! The New York air traffic controllers speak far too fast, the terminology is different, the names of places unfamiliar and, for a beginner on only his third trip after training, very confusing. His previous two trips had been to Africa and the Middle East where everything is so much more sedate.

'Why do they have to talk like quick-fire machineguns? I could hardly understand a word,' he replied.

'Wait 'till you try Chicago on a bad night,' muttered Len.

'You'll be OK. Just takes time to adapt,' I reassured him. 'I remember the first time I came here. Didn't know my arse from my elbow, and that was on Brits, flying at half the speed.'

'Skipper seemed happy enough though,' he replied. 'But I certainly needed your help, thanks for that.'

Harry Stoneham was one of our best

training captains — they did vary! He stood tall among men, it wasn't only his height and robust stature, but his demeanour too. At first sight, he seemed a little intimidating: medal ribbons below the wings on his substantial chest; a short, clipped moustache, thinning gingery hair brushed close to his scalp, and penetrating blue eyes. But when he smiled you saw the true man — friendly, authoritative, gentle, and with a depth of knowledge and understanding that quickly put less experienced men at their ease. I had known him for many years, he had been my instructor on Britannias and again on VC10s. He'd also been one of the first Comet captains. I liked him enormously.

Before our departure from London, he took me on one side and said, 'Alan's new. He's done a good course; I want to see how he copes at New York. I'm sure he can do it. I'll show him the likely arrival routes and take him through the ATC clearances we can expect. I'd like you to follow what he's doing on the R/T. Help him out a bit if he needs it.' In the event, as Harry expected, Alan did well.

At last Harry joined us, we ordered another round of Guinness and went to our table. 'Sorry I'm late. Got cornered by Dougie Barnes, fleet business. Well, have you chaps decided what to eat?'

The conversation turned to future plans. 'Dougie says we'll be going to the Far East soon, and across the Pacific too.'

'That'll give Seven Ohs a run for their money. They've had Australia for far too long.'

The conversation turned to the intense rivalry between us and the 707 fleet, they resented the worldwide publicity being given to the new VC10. Who would have the Sydney postings? Would there be a round-the-world service? How much time would we have off after each day's flying? What about the problems of fatigue; a constant trial when flying on long haul routes?

I could see Alan was becoming bored with this idle speculation. He was tired after our long trans-Atlantic flight. The time change was catching up with him, it was now well past midnight at home. He tried to suppress a yawn.

Len looked at him without much pity. 'If you think that was tiring, you should've been around in the old days.' And turning to Harry, 'D'you remember that Connie crash in Singapore? That was put down to fatigue.' And for Alan's benefit, 'They'd been on duty for well over 21 hours. The skipper misjudged it, came in too low. Hit the sea wall, undercarriage collapsed, wing broke off and they ended up upside down. Horrible it was, the cockpit crew had to escape through the DV window.'

'That was over ten years ago in '54. They put a limit on duty hours after that and based some crews in Sydney.' Harry explained to Alan. 'It's better these days.'

'And that wasn't all, mate of mine was the

flight engineer. His fiancée was the stewardess. She was with him. On her last trip before they were due to get married. She died later in hospital — from burns. The fire services were bloody useless. All the passengers were roasted to death upside down in their seats.'

My rare steak suddenly looked less appetising, 'Shall we change the subject?'

'Hasn't changed in some airlines neither,' Len continued, oblivious to what Alan might be thinking. 'Avianca did almost exactly the same in 1960 at Mo'Bay. Another Connie, coming down from here. It had to stop in Miami because of an engine problem. After an eight-hour delay, they continued to Mo'Bay and cocked up the approach. They came in too steep, hit the runway hard, buggered up the undercarriage and tore off a wing. It then turned upside down, caught fire and 37 people died, only five crew and four passengers survived. The cockpit crew escaped through the DV window; all the rest were toast. Almost a carbon copy of ours in Singapore. The stink of burning human flesh smelt like roast pork. The fire chief said ...'

'Thanks Len, I think we've heard enough,' said Harry mildly. 'We've all had our narrow escapes at times. Right now, I'd prefer to enjoy my dinner.'

I often wondered why flight crew seemed to enjoy such ghoulish stories about aviation accidents. Was it to bolster their own self-confidence; the 'it can't happen to me' syndrome? Or was it to show how brave they were? The details of accidents and their causes are well worth studying, you can learn a lot from others people's mistakes, but do we really need all the grisly details?

What, I thought, would Alan be thinking? Would he be fazed by Len's lurid accounts? We'd be going through Montego Bay tomorrow night, and the landing was known to be difficult in the dark. He said nothing on the walk back to the hotel, and neither were the accidents mentioned next morning at breakfast. It was one of those brisk sunny days you often have in spring, clear blue sky, a touch of frost and a chill wind blowing down the canyons between the skyscrapers. After we'd finished our coffees and paid the check, Alan said he was going for a walk in Central Park, he needed some fresh air. I went over to Fifth to browse in Barnes & Noble before taking an afternoon nap. Len said he was going to look for some tools.

◊◊◊

That evening, out at the airport in the briefing room, Harry asked us which of the three legs we would each like to fly, the first one to Nassau, the second to Montego Bay or the last one over the mountains to Kingston? I said whichever was going, Alan said the first one to Nassau. When Harry asked why, he explained because it was flat, no mountains like Jamaica, and he didn't fancy the night landing into Montego Bay.

'In that case David can take us down to Nassau and you can fly us into Mo'Bay. No need to look so worried, I'll talk you through it.'

'But, Sir ...'

'No buts. Dave, can you find us some approach charts, and a map of Jamaica if there is one.'

I then found myself listening to one of the most lucid descriptions I have ever heard of how to fly this particular visual approach and landing. Jamaica, Harry explained, lies in the region of the northeast trades which is why the runway is aligned on zero six zero degrees magnetic. It lies along the coast only a few feet above sea level on what used to be swampy land. The threshold starts virtually on the beach with the centre-line approach lights set on poles out in the sea. There are no approach aids other than an NDB (a low powered radio beacon) on the airfield, positioned some way out to the left from the runway. At night, you must judge the descent towards the runway using only the perspective view of the converging runway edge lights. Since the approach path is over the sea, there are no visual cues on the surface below to aid depth perception. The result is a visual illusion which can make you feel higher than you really are. If you are not ready for it, it's easy to be misled into flying too low. Several air accidents have been caused by this problem. Pilots know it as a 'black-hole' approach.

'That's the bad news,' said Harry with a smile, 'The good news is I'll show you how to avoid the trap. You see this little promontory here on the coast, it's almost exactly six miles from the runway.' And putting his finger on the map. 'There's a posh hotel, Round Hill, here on the coast. It's well-lit, tonight's forecast is good, so you'll see it easily. It also shows up well on the radar as we come down from the north. If you aim for that and descend to 1,800 feet, it'll put you below the clouds if there are any around. When you are three miles short of the coast, start a shallow turn towards the runway and continue to descend so you are at 1,500 feet here.' And he pointed to a position just to the east of the promontory.

I saw that Len was listening intently.

'At the end of the turn, you will be almost exactly five miles out from the runway. This will give you a good 'starting gate' at the correct height and distance from the threshold. It's always best for any visual approach at night to find a suitable gate. Then all you need do is to 'fix' the perspective view of the runway in your mind and continue down towards it, keeping that image constant all the way down. With me so far?

'Now comes the interesting bit. Think about it — you've been descending from the north, you can see this promontory ahead at Round Hill, the wind has been blowing steadily from over your left shoulder at about twenty knots. But just as you're finishing the turn, it suddenly changes and blows from the south, quite strongly at times. Then, as you descend further, and come within three miles of the runway it changes back, coming again from the northeast. If you are not ready for it, it screws up your alignment with the runway just as you are trying to establish the correct descent path. Any ideas why?'

Alan shook his head.

'Well, if you think back to your Met lessons, you'll remember at night the land will have cooled, causing a classic land breeze. The problem here is that it funnels down this valley like a river. Once you are within about three miles of the runway, you are beyond that torrent of air and everything comes back to normal again. Sounds complicated, but I'll show you the signs to look out for.'

I dug Alan in the ribs. 'Piece of cake as they say. I'll go out now and start the checks. See you on the aircraft.' Len came out too, but not before warning Alan to watch out for the undertaker's wind.

'What did you do that for?' I asked him. 'And you really shouldn't tell such gory stories over dinner.'

'Nothing really, I'll explain later. He's a good lad.' He grunted, 'But needs toughening up a bit.'

The leg down to Nassau was all very straightforward, I'd done it several times before. On the ground during the refuelling, Alan took over from me in the co-pilot's seat so he could fly the next leg to Montego Bay. After take-off, as we were passing over Cuba, Harry left us to it for a while and went back to talk to the passengers. I took his seat. 'A little arithmetic can help too. Here, look at this,' I said to Alan, passing him a piece of paper with a diagram of the approach and some calculations. 'One fifty knots; two and half miles per minute. If you start the stopwatch at the end of the turn, five miles from touchdown, after sixty seconds you should be halfway down, at around seven fifty feet. You may need to make some adjustments as you go down the slope, it's only approximate. The headwind will make the groundspeed a little slower. But it all helps your visual judgement.'

I could see Alan puzzling over a few more calculations as Harry came back and reclaimed his seat. 'I'll leave you to decide the top of descent point,' he told Alan, 'But, I'd start down about ten miles earlier than usual, that'll give you time to get the checklists out of the way before you start the turn. Then you'll have more time to concentrate on your height and distance as you line up with the runway.'

◊◊◊

'Can you see the field? Over there, slightly to the left,' said Harry, pointing towards the lights of Montego Bay. And to ATC, 'Montego Approach, Speedbird 683, we have the field in sight, we'd like to position for a visual contact approach.'

'Right,' thought Alan, 'This is it. Concentrate. No time for mistakes. 5,000 feet and 20 miles to the coast, better start slowing to 210 knots. 'There — speed's good.' Then out loud, 'Flaps twenty and approach check.'

'If you turn now about ten degrees right,' said Harry, 'You'll be heading straight for Round Hill. Can you see the lights, that's the hotel? Radar's showing ten miles to the coast. I'd bring it back to 180 knots now if I were you.' 2,000 feet. Looks about right. Better call for the landing check.'

'Landing check, gear down please.'

'Gear down, three greens,' they all checked. Harry changed frequency and called the tower for landing clearance. 'OK Alan? You're cleared to land. That's 1,800 feet and three miles, start the turn now, about twenty degrees of bank should do it. And start easing down to 1,500 feet.'

Alan started the turn. 'Keep it going . . . keep it going.' And leaning forward for a better look, 'There's the runway. Nearly there, straighten up now. 1,500 feet, remember the stopwatch, bring the speed back to 150 knots.'

'Landing flap.'

Harry moved the flap lever as asked and said, 'Can you feel we're drifting slightly right? In a moment you'll see that suddenly change to a drift to the left. There she blows. Quick, lay it off to the right — about five degrees should do it. A little more. Keep descending just as you are. It's looking good. The drift's coming off.'

'Landing check complete, landing flap set,' called Len.

'I'll show him. Won't let his horror stories put me off. And what was that Dave said about the timing? Damn, missed it, but seems alright.'

'There you are,' said Harry, 'All lined up, speed's good and nicely on the slope.'

Alan concentrated on the runway ahead. He was determined to touch down in the right place. 'Steady now. Steady, don't go low. Watch the speed.' Sweat ran down his forehead and dripped off the end of his nose. He tried to ignore it. 'Keep it coming,' he muttered to himself.

The single row of approach lights slid under the nose, 'Ooof! That surf looks close. There's the beach, we're over the threshold, over the runway, ease off the power, gently now, raise the nose, just a fraction, not too much.' He felt a small bump and then a rumble, 'We're down, lower the nose, wait 'till the nosewheel touches.' 'Spoilers — reverse power.'

Harry pulled the speedbrake lever and selected idle reverse and then reverse power. Alan pressed on the brake pedals and slowed to taxi speed, then continued to the turning circle near the end of the runway so he could back track towards taxiway that led to the terminal building. The marshaller guided him to their parking place, he stopped the aircraft, called for the shutdown checks, looked at Harry and smiled.

'Well done. Wasn't so bad was it? How would you like to do the next leg as well? Over the mountains to Kingston.' This was unheard of, two legs in a row.

'Yes please, sir.'

'I won't talk you round this time, I'll leave you to make all you own decisions. Only one word of advice, if you're too high after coming over the mountains and don't feel comfortable with making a straight-in, fly over the field and do a standard right hand circuit. That way you'll know exactly where you are when you start your approach. It'll be just like your training at Shannon.'

It only takes thirty minutes to fly from

Montego Bay to Kingston. There are two routes over the mountains, this time ATC cleared us along the north coast towards Ocho Rios, climbing to 13,000 feet before turning south towards Kingston. It's a busy half hour. Alan would have to be on his mettle. Once again, he proved he was up to it. He came over the Kingston beacon at 5,000 feet and, as Harry had advised, asked for a visual right-hand circuit, descended to 1,500 feet on the downwind leg parallel with the runway, started the stopwatch and after, sixty seconds, turned back towards the runway, perfectly positioned for the approach and landing. All textbook stuff, exactly as taught during training.

Even Len was impressed.

◊◊◊

In the 1960s, the flight deck crew stayed at Morgan's Harbour, the cabin crew in a hotel in town. Our driver picked us up outside the terminal in an old black Chevvy with outrageous fins and too much chrome. The inside was all red plastic — sticky in the warm humid air. We ambled gently along the Palisadoes road towards Port Royal, a calypso playing on the radio, the driver dangling an arm languidly out of the window in the cool gentle breeze of our motion. Even though the sea air smelt of decaying seaweed and rotting fish, it was a welcome relief after the heat of the terminal.

Morgan's Harbour is a small, relaxed hotel by the sea, at least, it was in those days. There's an open-air bar, a sitting out area with tables and umbrellas, and a swimming pool which had once been an old careening dock. Its bottom is made of large slate slabs brought out from England as ballast in sailing ships. On the opposite side of the pool there is a brick-built changing room, which I was told, had once been a gunpowder store. But best of all, the bar staff always kept a plate of sandwiches and a cold-box full of beer ready for our arrival.

We arrived shortly before midnight and found the place nearly empty. Len fetched the essential supplies from behind the bar and we relaxed under the stars enjoying Red Stripes from the tin and thick brown bread crab sandwiches. 'That was a good day's work,' said Harry, 'You did well, young Alan.'

'Not bad for a beginner.' I smiled.

'And you escaped the undertaker's wind,' said Len.

'What do you mean? Were you winding me up? Trying to put me off? I've heard enough stories about Mo'Bay without you adding to them.'

Len looked aggrieved. 'Let me tell you something. I've seen things which would turn your stomach, I bet Harry has too. I used to be the ground engineer here before I went flying. We covered both Montego Bay and the airport here at Kingston, the Strats had the route then. Big piston engines always going wrong — and other things too. Long before your time.' He swigged some of his beer. 'Got to know Jamaica well. Beautiful place, but the locals are very superstitious — *Obeah* men casting spells in the hills, duppies coming to haunt you.'

'What're duppies?'

'The evil spirits of the dead.'

'Do they still believe it?'

'Oh yes. After that Connie crash, the locals couldn't get rid of them. Perhaps it was the smell — or they didn't do the right rituals for the dead.'

'But do you believe it?'

'Not really, but sometimes I do wonder. It gets to you after dark. 'Duppy know who fi frighten,' they say. And sometimes it even got to me.'

'And what was all that about the undertaker's wind?'

Len paused, 'That's the wind in the night. It blows the stink of death out to sea.'

At Death's Door

I was in the middle of calling San Juan Oceanic Control when Gordon Brookes, our chief steward, came into the cockpit. I only heard part of what he said, but it started with, 'Captain, we have a problem.' This galvanised, our captain, 'Pip' Garner, who interrupted my call on the R/T, with an abrupt, 'Mind the ship 'til I get back,' before leaping out of his seat and disappearing down the back.

'What was all that about?' I asked Malcolm who was sitting behind me at the flight engineer's station.

'Some bloke dying in the cabin,' he answered without looking up from his fuel calculations.

We were on our way from Barbados on the long eight-hour flight across the middle of the Atlantic back to London. I figured a little preparatory work might not go amiss, so asked young Adam Newbold, at the nav table, where he thought we would be in ten minutes time. I also called San Juan and told them we might soon have a medical emergency and to standby. Meanwhile, could they get us the latest Bermuda and Santa Maria weather? I guessed Pip would want to know these things when he returned from the cabin.

'Twenty-six north, fifty-two west,' replied Adam.

'How far would that put us from Bermuda or back to Barbados?'

After a few calculations, he passed me a note; 780 nautical miles to go back, the same to divert to Bermuda, and another 1,500 if we continue to The Azores. 'What d'you think he'll do?' he asked.

'Well, if Bermuda's still good, I'd go there. But let's see what Pip has to say.'

A few minutes later, San Juan came back on the blower with the Bermuda and Santa Maria weather. Bermuda was clear with a gentle south-easterly breeze, but Santa Maria was blowing a gale — forty knots plus from the south-west, with low cloud and rain, and right across the runway.

The Azores would not be a promising proposition. Then Jenny Hay, our first class stewardess (in both senses of the phrase), popped in looking her usual glamorous self. 'Full aircraft, just started dinner, and then this old geezer goes and pops his clogs. Gordon has found a doctor, he's examining him now. So, I've brought you boys some tea while the going's good. Guess it'll soon be very busy. Galley's in chaos.'

I jotted down the weather reports for Bermuda and Santa Maria, together with the note from Adam with the distances and passed them to her, saying, 'Give these to the captain, would you? Thanks.'

Ten minutes later, Pip came back looking ashen, he was breathless and somewhat dishevelled, 'I fear he's a goner, nothing the doc could do. We gave him oxygen, tried CPR but he's a large man, too heavy, difficult to move from his seat, and by the time we finally did get him out, it was too late. Thanks for your note on the weather. I don't think there's much point in diverting, best to keep going to London. What do you all think?

'Is his wife with him?'

'No, only his son — taking his father to see a heart specialist in London.' Pip drank his tea, asked for another and sat quietly in his seat.

'Well, he won't need that now,' I suggested, 'What does his son say?'

'Haven't broached that one yet, the doc is talking to him now. I'll go back in a moment and see what they both think. Have you said anything to ATC?'

'Only to ask for those weather reports and to warn them we might soon have a medical emergency on our hands, I said to standby.'

'Well done. Let's leave it at that for the time being. If they ask, tell them we're still evaluating the situation. Think I'll go back now and see what's happening.'

After Pip had gone, Malcolm rubbed his huge hands together and said, 'Exceedingly inconsiderate to muck up dinner, if you ask me, bad manners and all that. Might have waited until they'd finished. But I'm sure dining with a stiff will improve their appetites. Dracula would most certainly approve.'

'Oh do shut up, Malc.' I had flown with him many times before and knew him to be a good operator. I liked his wicked sense of humour, but somehow, his taste for the macabre didn't seem appropriate right now. Jenny returned and asked for the Voyage Report folders, as the captain needed to fill out the report forms for recording a death. 'How is he?' I asked.

'Who, captain or casualty? Our punter is — shall we say — stone cold sober. Our captain is his usual self'

Pip Garner is one of my favourite captains. He is short and wiry, always active and very fit. He has that economy of movement and natural modesty that is the hallmark of a man who really knows his business. Better still, from a co-pilot's point of view, he is always generous in giving away landings.

As is so often the case in the airlines, I'd never met Adam before, but he seemed a quiet and sensible enough young man. Malcolm Scobie, on the other hand, is entirely different, loud, a giant of a man, good prop forward material, I should think, but not entirely diplomatic. I remember one occasion when I was new to it all and still a trainee navigator, he gave me his idea of good advice, 'You know, there are only two dangerous things on this aircraft,' and after pointing to the two pilots, 'Those two blokes sitting up there.' The captain was not amused. But, like all good flight engineers, he could fix almost anything.

And so we waited. I called San Juan, then New York Oceanic with our time and position at the FIR boundary. San Juan had already notified New York of our possible medical problem. They asked if we wanted to divert and I said no, not yet, we were continuing as planned, but that might change. Then Pip reappeared.

'Malcolm, we've decided to put him in one of the toilets. We can't leave him where he is, not in a full aircraft while they start serving dinner again. I don't have the strength to lift him, so can I ask you to help Gordon carry him down the back. He's grossly overweight, I reckon the two of you will be able to manage OK. Should be a doddle for a big strong fellow like you.'

'Captain,' said Malcolm rising from his seat and standing to mock attention, 'Since you ask so nicely, I shall be happy to oblige. Your kindly aeronautical undertakers, Scobie and Brookes, at your service — Sah!' And with a theatrical salute, he departed to do the deed.

◊◊◊

'Right Gordon, what's the deal?' Malcolm looked at the cold grey corpse lying flat on the floor, the doctor kneeling beside the head and

Gordon holding the therapeutic oxygen bottle and mask. It was clear the victim was beyond help. He was a large man, almost filling the aisle. Gordon suggested Malcolm should take the feet, which were nearest him, while he and the doctor lifted the shoulders, but the body kept slipping out of their hands and falling back to the floor.

'Perhaps we should change ends? I'm stronger than you two,' Malcolm suggested. 'Stand back and I'll step over towards you.' He tried not to trip on the exposed belly. 'Bugger,' he gasped, 'Nearly got him in the balls.'

Passengers averted their gaze. The doctor and Gordon were more nimble on their feet. One of the stewards cleared a path down the aisle towards the tail, removing the first aid kit, oxygen bottles, blankets, and pillows while the two stewardesses pushed the serving trolleys back into the galley.

'Two, six, heave.' It was all Malcolm could do to raise and hold the man's shoulders, the head and arms kept flopping around, there was nothing solid to hold on to. And he found it wasn't easy walking backwards. One arm swung out to one side, bumping against the seats as they struggled down the aisle. The next stage was even more difficult, how to keep the toilet door open while manoeuvring the body onto the seat? How to fasten it in place? Malcom grasped the body around the chest in a tight embrace, 'Shall we dance?' He muttered, as he managed to seat it on the loo.

But it kept falling over. 'Quick, someone get me some seatbelt extenders,' he puffed. He then tied some nautical lashings between a grab handle, the seat and the washbasin taps to secure the body in place. Then he stepped back to admire his knots, 'That should fix him. Looks pretty good sitting on the throne like that, he could almost be alive.' And turning to one of the stewardesses, 'Stop gawping like that, why don't you give the stiff a stiff drink?'

'Shush,' hissed Gordon as he closed and locked the door so no passengers could enter. Then, to the two stewardesses, 'Come on you two, let's get moving with the trolleys, we need to get those dinners out.'

But as they made their way back up the aisle, Malcolm couldn't resist it, 'Anyone else have the prawns tonight?'

◊◊◊

Once back on the flight deck, he reported, 'All done captain, he's sitting comfortably upon the throne — aft heads, port side, away from the galley, and lashed well down.' Malcolm is ex-navy, 'We've locked the door, so he won't trouble anyone. And d'you know, some of the punters never even woke up when we carried him down the aisle.'

'Thanks,' said Pip, 'Now back to business. Phil, you'd better tell Oceanic we will be continuing to London, there's no need to divert, and I'll call Speedbird London and ask them to advise Ops Control we'll be arriving with a dead passenger. And when I've done that, I'll go round the cabin and see how everyone is feeling, I don't want to make a PA announcement and wake everyone up, some are already asleep. Better to leave them in peace. And then there are all these reports.'

Once again, dear Jenny popped in, this time our ministering angel came carrying a large pot of tea and some sandwiches. 'Gordon said you might need these after all that excitement.'

I turned to Pip, 'Captain, I'm very happy minding the ship for as long as you want. The three of us can look after it, and you've got enough to do with all that paperwork and reassuring the passengers. I guess some will be feeling a bit shook up. And you look as though you could do with a break too.'

He looked at me gratefully, finished his tea and said, 'Thanks, I'll take a walk around first before I tackle the reports.' With that he tidied himself up, donned his uniform cap and jacket, and disappeared.

Gordon stuck his head round the flight deck door, 'Malcolm, a word in your ear, you'll need to prepare your excuses. The captain's getting an earful from a gent who says he overheard your little joke. Thought I'd better warn you.'

'But I only whispered, "did anyone else have the prawns."'

'Problem is, your whispering sounds like shouting.' So true, I thought. When Pip returned to his seat, he said nothing, just busied himself writing the reports. There's a lot of paperwork when flying, especially when someone dies — aircraft run on kerosene, airlines run on paper. When he had finished, he handed it all to me, saying, 'Here, it could do with being checked by another pair of eyes. And you never know, one day when you're a captain, it might happen to you.'

'Was the doctor willing to certify the death?'

'No, he says that will have to be done in London, but he has given me a letter stating his opinion, here — take a look. The port health doctors will need to examine the body when we arrive. Something to do with infectious diseases.' Then, after a short pause, 'Malcolm.'

'Yes sir.'

'We now have yet another problem. What exactly did you say back there? Something to do with the prawns, was it? Seems one of the passengers overheard, says he's a manager or something in the catering firm that supplies the meals. And he hasn't taken kindly to you blaming their prawn salads. Says it was a slanderous remark, he'll be writing to the Chairman.'

'But it was only a harmless little joke with Gordon, very quiet like. You need a little black humour in this job.'

'Well, you may have gone a little too far this time. Let's hope he doesn't write the letter, he may have cooled down by the time we reach London.'

I noticed Pip didn't eat much that night. And so we droned on through the night. Jenny cleared our meal trays away, the hours passed slowly by, Adam was up and down all night busy with the sextant, taking his astro shots, and I tried to remain awake between routine position reports to ATC; New York, then Santa Maria and finally Shanwick Oceanic Control.

A few wisps of cirrus high above began to glow pink, the sky gradually turned dove grey, suddenly a shaft of gold shot out from over to my right and I tried to blot it out with a chart folded over the inadequate sun visors provided as original equipment by a generous Mr Vickers.

'Not long now,' said Jenny who had joined us for a quiet sit-down on the jump seat before she needed to start on the breakfasts in the first class cabin. 'Funny thing,' she said, 'Not many people wanted the prawns last night. I wonder why that was.' 'Unfortunately,' said Pip, looking pointedly at Malcolm, 'Word always spreads when you least want it to.'

Our arrival into London on a typical grey winter's morning was as uneventful as usual — that is, until the police and port health doctors came on board. Pip made an announcement to the passengers explaining what had happened, offering condolences to the man's son, and saying there would be a short delay while the doctors checked the casualty. But, when Gordon tried to open the toilet door to let the doctors in, he found it wouldn't budge. Malcolm had to be called to the rescue.

Unfortunately these doors open inwards. Rigor mortis had started to set in, and the body, now stiffly set in a seated position had slipped from the lashings and toppled to the floor where it was jammed between the throne and the door. Malcolm had to break it down with a crash that could be heard even in the cockpit. And if that was not enough, poor Pip, who had by now moved to the door where the passengers were disembarking, was told in no uncertain terms that he would not be hearing the last of it.

What next? I wondered as we left in the crew bus.

◊◊◊

Barely a week later, I was in Crew Reporting, busy signing in for another trip, this time to Bahrain.

'Weren't you on that Barbados trip, the one when a passenger died in mid-Atlantic?' I looked up to where one of the clerks behind the counter was holding up the front page of *The Daily Nation.*

'One of your blokes picked this up when he was out there soon after your little escapade. Seems it was quite a drama.'

The Daily Nation is the Barbadian equivalent

of the UK's *Daily Mail*. The headline read: Poisoned by Prawns: Sudden Death in The Skies, and the article began:

> **Disaster Strikes BOAC Flight to London**
> Tragedy stalked the passengers and crew on board the BOAC Super VC10 Flight 690. 'Men died' said a passenger, 'We were thousands of miles from anywhere, beyond all hope of help.' 'We were too frightened to eat,' said another, 'I blame the prawns, it nearly ended in disaster'. Emergency doctors swarmed onto the aircraft when it landed at London Airport, and people were rushed to hospital. BOAC and Sunshine Foods have declined to comment, but our fearless reporters will uncover the truth so that all Barbadians will know what really happened.

'Sensationalist rubbish,' and then I told him what had really happened.

'I bet old Malcolm Scobie was called into the "headmaster's study" for a bollocking,' he said. And indeed he was.

I was in Nairobi when I met Malcolm again, he was with another crew staying in the same hotel. Over a few beers, he told me what had transpired. Only one day after we arrived home from Barbados, the manager had demanded his presence in the office. As expected, he was torn off a strip in no uncertain terms. The manager read him out a long list of all the problems he had caused.

Both the *Daily Mail* and *Express* in the UK

had picked up on the story, quoting some of the passengers who said they were so frightened they dared not touch the food. Another complained he'd had nothing to eat for eight whole hours, and hadn't even been offered a free drink in recompense. What if the pilot had died, they asked?

Sunshine Foods had phoned the Chairman threatening to sue BOAC. He, in turn, called the flight manager who then phoned Captain Garner at home requiring an explanation. Letters had been written, one to the caterers expressing the airline's total confidence in their products, and regretting how the matter had been blown out of all proportion. But the Chairman's real ire had descended upon *The Daily Nation.* He demanded they print a full and complete apology in bold print on the front page of their wretched rag, giving the true facts and praising the efforts of the doctor and crew for doing everything possible to save the dying man. Furthermore, he recommended the editor should, in future, pursue the truth and not print downright lies.

When I pressed him, Malcolm did admit it was not the first time he had been in hot water for unguarded remarks. His manager, he said, had also reprimanded him for breaking down the toilet door, why had he not called the ground engineers? A letter would be placed on his personal file, saying, if there was ever a next time, disciplinary action would follow.

'Bloody rumours, bloody reporters, and bloody managers,' he moaned.

'Here, have another beer. From little jokes great troubles grow.'

'Cheers! Trouble is they all make mountains out of bloody molehills,' he retorted. 'I've seen enough death and destruction to recognise real trouble when I see it. I'd be pleased to eat all their prawns if it would make them happy.'

His First Command

He had survived the tribulations of the command course. Hours in the simulator practising emergency procedures, then having to prove he knew how to use them under the critical eyes of the check captains. Base flying at Prestwick, with endless circuits and bumps on four, three and even two engines, and other unlikely manoeuvres such as flapless landings. Also, up to high altitude to experience Dutch rolls, stalls and emergency descents. Followed by a check ride — a highly artificial route flight to Shannon, 'with problems' — in his view a ridiculous game — a pretend bomb warning, various flight instrument failures and, of course, the obligatory engine failures. But he managed to pass them all.

After that, four long route flights with supervisory captains so he could practise and demonstrate his competence — out east to Hong Kong, then to Australia, Africa, the Middle East, followed by a route check across the Atlantic to New York and Bermuda. Finally, a pep-talk from the flight manager, before collecting his new jacket with the four gold rings on the sleeves. Now, it is his first trip in command. In his own mind, this is the real test.

Roderick Baird, 35, lean, fair-haired and with the well-tanned face of a sailor, kisses his wife and children goodbye before setting off along the A30 to Heathrow. The drive from Bagshot on this warm July morning will only take half an hour.

He begins automatically to check the conditions. Wind from the west, 15 knots, judging by those trees over there. Take-off at 12.30. Wonder how full it'll be? Flight time to Bermuda, seven hours plus, near max weight. He leans forward to peer up out of the windscreen, cloud base around 3,000 feet I guess, fair weather cumulus — damn! Must look where I'm going, only just missed that cyclist. Won't do that again. Nearing Egham, the traffic slows, road works? No, just a temporary hold-up. A clear run up to Hatton Cross and the BOAC hangars. Who will be on my crew? Will they know it's my first time? What should I tell them?

The crew shuttle bus takes him to Terminal 3, south wing. Up the stairs to flight briefing, I'm early — deliberately so. 'Crew list, captain?' He takes a look. Ah! Don Clifford is the senior first officer, someone I've known on and off for years. Geoff Long, the first officer, don't know him at all, he'll be navigating. Ivan Pickford, the senior engineer officer, know him slightly, an older man, balding, with a moustache if I remember rightly.

He goes into the small room where the manuals are kept — the latest orders and crew notices, recent bulletins, the latest amendments to procedures. Good; nothing has changed. Then along to flight planning where crews are briefed on the weather, route and fuel requirements. Think I'll go through it all before the others arrive. 'Do you have the stuff for flight two six five — Bermuda?'

'Nearly ready, captain. Here's the Met folder to be getting on with, they're just finalising the fuel plan now, only take a few minutes.'

Oh shit! Just my luck. Dirty great hurricane. Better examine this carefully. About 100 miles northeast of the island — hmmm — travelling north. The wind's over 40 knots across the runway. But the forecast looks better. Hope it'll be OK by the time we get there, I'll check with the planners.

Mary, the lady who does the briefings, comes over, 'Morning captain. Baird isn't it? Congratulations, this your first outing?'

He smiles and nods, 'This cross-wind looks a bit much.'

'Don't worry, the forecast's OK for your ETA. The hurricane is well to the north. I've checked with the Met Office. Here, take a look at the plan. We've given you a route that goes further south than usual. To be well clear of the bad weather.'

'Thanks, I'll check through it before the others arrive.'

Out to Land's End, that's normal enough, then across the pond. Only slightly longer than the great circle. 'Can I see a North Atlantic plotting chart please? Thanks. What did you say was the position of the hurricane?'

He plots the centre on the chart. 35 North, 63 30 West. We'll be coming in from the east, about 150 miles from there, and it's moving north. Should be OK. 'Morning, captain.' Interrupted from his calculations, he looks up to see two smiling faces. Don and Geoff introduce themselves.

Don is tall with dark hair and a thin serious face, he smokes a pipe with an air of being much older than his thirty-odd years, almost middle-aged, in fact. Geoff looks as if he doesn't need to shave yet, but that's unfair.

He shakes their hands, 'Just been looking at the plan, we have a hurricane to avoid.' And he shows them what he has plotted. 'Who's navigating today?'

'I am, sir' says Geoff. 'May I take a look?'

While he does so, Baird talks through the problems with Don. Neither of them like the look of it, the forecast surface wind at Kindley Field is from 330 degrees at 40 knots gusting 45. 'Let me do a quick calculation,' Don says. 'On runway three zero, allowing for the magnetic variation, that's 45 degrees off the runway heading which means,' and he looks at a graph, 'A cross-wind component of just over 28 knots, bit tight, but should be OK.'

'Captain Baird?' It's Ivan Pickford, the flight

engineer. 'Hope I'm not too late.' Pickford is well into his fifties, a bustling busy sort of man with sharp eyes. They shake hands. 'Missed the shuttle bus.' He mops his head with a large handkerchief.

Baird talks through the problems with the flight planner and his crew, the position of the hurricane, their planned route, the cross-wind right on limits, the reliability of the forecast, possible diversions to Halifax or New York, and whether they will be able to load any extra fuel.

Mary says it's a normal plan, using island reserve fuel (that's two hours' worth of fuel — New York being too far away for a normal diversion). We may be able to squeeze a little more on for you, depending on the final load. Ivan says he'd better go out to the aircraft and asks for the final fuel figure. Baird gives it to him and says to keep the bowsers standing by. Then he turns to Geoff,

'When we get going and we're settled in the cruise, I'd like you, please, to work out two positions for me; the last point at which we can divert from altitude to Halifax and the same for New York. Then, if we don't like the weather, we'll just carry on and give Bermuda a miss. What do you think, Don?'

All three pilots are qualified navigators, it seems sensible to put their heads together. If the weather's still dodgy and they can't land, they won't have enough fuel to descend, take a look and climb back up to altitude, the best option will be to stay in the cruise and fly round the hurricane from the positions that Geoff will work out. He looks at Geoff, 'I expect Don has told you, this is my first trip in command. Just my luck to meet a ruddy hurricane first time out!'

As they walk out across the tarmac to their VC10, Baird feels a little apprehensive, but wears a mask of confidence. Aboard the aircraft, he finds the chief steward is Guy Ponting, a man he knows of old. 'Congratulations, sir. Celebrations in Bermuda, is it? Brown milk or champers?' The rest of the cabin crew are new to him. He takes Guy aside, tells him about the hurricane and explains what he proposes to do. 'It should be well to the north, if not, the celebrations will be in New York.'

He takes comfort in the usual routine of flight preparation, the passengers come on board, the dispatcher shows him the loadsheet, they can squeeze an extra three tonnes of fuel on board, if that would help, 'I've delayed a consignment of electrical goods, Mary phoned with that idea. We'll put it on tomorrow's flight, the timing's not critical.' Baird thanks him. 'Ivan — go down and give the refuellers the new fuel figure, would you.' Good thing I asked him to keep the bowser standing by. Must thank Mary next time I see her.

Well, it's a nice day, next bit's easy. Take-off to the west, normal departure, down to Land's End and then out over the Atlantic, passing ninety miles south of Ireland. Seven hours, twenty minutes, over the water. Far from land.

Nearing Land's End, Geoff calls Shanwick and obtains their oceanic clearance. Time passes. Geoff says the Loran is good today. Don listens out to the weather broadcasts from New York, the Bermuda reports come up every half hour. Everything depends on them. What will the winds do? Hope they abate. Ivan reports slightly up on fuel. Anne, our stewardess brings lunch, she asks about the hurricane. Guy says the passengers are happy, but a few are asking questions, he has told them it is moving away. 'I'll let them know what is happening when we are nearer and know what we've decided, no point in worrying them yet,' Baird replies. 'I'll take a turn round the cabin when I've had my lunch.'

Halfway now, nearing ocean weather ship Delta. Geoff gives them a call to check his position. Only three hours to go. Baird calls Speedbird London on HF radio, asking them to telephone the BOAC station manager in Bermuda. He wants him to report on the weather. We'll keep a listening watch on SELCAL, he tells them. He puts on his new jacket. 'There's posh for you,' says Ivan as Baird goes back to talk to the passengers. Most are dozing after their meal. One gentleman, who clearly knows a thing or two and lives in Bermuda, wants to know what we plan to do. Baird tells him the facts. He understands. Someone else overhears and asks how dangerous the hurricane really is. 'It's only a small one, we'll be keeping well out of its way.' The steward and stewardesses down the back are tucking into their meal. He doesn't disturb them, other than to say things are going well — they know about the hurricane, Guy has briefed them.

Back in the cockpit, Geoff shows him the two positions he has worked out. If they turn at 62 West and take a straight line to Halifax that will put them too close to the storm clouds around the hurricane. Baird suggests the decision point should be 190 miles earlier at 59 West. Geoff's turn point for New York is much nearer Bermuda. He says it is difficult to estimate because they will be facing strong headwinds coming from the northwest when they go round the far side of the storm.

The Met chart lacks sufficient detail. Baird asks him to assume a wider sweep to the west and calculate a conservative fuel estimate, starting from part way down the descent. 'We'll continue towards Bermuda and make the decision as we near your minimum fuel figure,' he says. He discusses the plan with Don and Ivan. Don is happy. Ivan not so sure, he wants to keep going to New York.

Speedbird London calls. The station manager has reported it's still blowing hard with heavy rain. Not much change, but it is improving. Baird asks that he reports every hour, and to let him know of any change. Not much more he can do right now, other than bite his fingernails.

They come to the first decision point, just over an hour to go. 'Continue.' New York weather is good, Bermuda's getting better. In half an hour, they'll be able to talk to Bermuda ATC on VHF. How slowly time passes, he thinks. 180 miles to go. 'Try them now,' he says to Don. No luck.

There's quite a lot of static, even on the VHF. More minutes pass by. Success. Don gives them the ETA and asks for the latest weather report. Still raining but the wind has slackened. 'How's the fuel?' Baird asks Ivan.

'You still have another ten minutes before Geoff's minimum. Wouldn't we do better on runway zero one? It's into wind.'

'Too short, and probably slippery in this heavy rain.' Top of descent, they start down. Time is nearly up. Don asks Bermuda if there's any change.

No.

'We continue. Everyone happy?' Don nods, and says OK. They fly on down into the gathering dusk. Ivan stares at the fuel gauges. 'That's it. We're committed now,' he mutters under his breath. Baird knows it too.

Passing 10,000 feet, despite the rain, they see a flash of light ahead. It becomes clearer, one white flash every two seconds. 'St David's lighthouse, it's less than a mile from the threshold of runway three zero,' says Don. ATC has them identified on radar. They accept vectors to the approach. The runway lights come into sight. Despite the wind, the air is smooth, but as they come down through 500 feet, it becomes quite bumpy. Wind from the right. Over fifteen degrees of drift.

They come into the flare. Baird pushes the rudder to straighten up. They're down. Windscreen wipers flapping like crazy. They taxi to the end, turn off towards the terminal and shut down. Anne appears right on cue. 'Guy thought you deserve these.' And she hands round four glasses of champagne. Don leans across the centre console, 'Cheers.' Ivan raises his glass too, 'Not bad for a beginner,' and adds more quietly, 'I suppose.'

'Thanks everyone,' Baird replies, 'Good team effort, and a special thanks to Geoff for all his calculations — and for finding Bermuda.'

A very wet station officer comes on board. 'Very glad to see you. You're the first in after the storm. It's been quite a day.'

'And for us too.'

On the drive to the Princess Hotel, a large pink painted building in Hamilton looking south across the bay, Don says, 'Party's in my room.'

'Thanks, but I need a bath first. Won't be long.'

When Baird arrives in Don's room, he finds the other three already there. Pity the cabin crew aren't here too, they stay in another hotel on St George's, at the other end of the island. Don appears with a bottle of champagne. He has filled his basin with ice so it's well chilled.

'Present from Guy,' he says. 'Cheers —

and to mangle a famous quote, 'It is a truth universally acknowledged, that a pilot on his first command, is in want of better weather.'' They laugh. The champagne tastes good, even out of tooth mugs.

'Or,' says Ivan, heavy with meaning, 'A damn close run thing.'

They finish the champagne and order some beers from room service. Ivan says he prefers whisky, he has a half bottle in his pocket. After one beer, Baird suddenly feels very tired, 'Sorry chaps, I really do need to go to bed. Night, all. See you in the morning.'

Was it really that close? His mind won't let go. He keeps going over his decisions. Were they justified? Geoff had worked the fuel plan backwards from New York, starting with the final reserve, back round the hurricane, even adding an extra 50 knots of headwind, and giving it a wider berth than strictly necessary. Baird knows, he checked it with him. We could probably have gone even lower before climbing back and going on to New York. But how far? Sleep escapes him.

What's up with Ivan? Why's he unhappy? Or am I imagining it? What if the wind across the runway had increased? What could I have done then?

Next morning, he has a late breakfast in his room. Night flight tonight — Nassau and Mexico City. Then back to Bermuda the following day. Think I'll have Don in the co-pilot's seat into Mexico, the ATC can be difficult. He takes a walk round Hamilton to clear his mind, then goes back to the hotel for an afternoon's rest. Won't sleep, but better than nothing.

On the ride to the airport, he explains, as a new captain, he is not allowed to give away landings, but offers Don the leg to Nassau on the understanding he hands back control as they pass 500 feet on the approach. He also asks him to do the co-piloting on the leg to Mexico City, 'I need someone who's familiar with their broken English. Then tomorrow Geoff can fly us back to Nassau on the same basis.' Under the circumstances, that is the best he can do. He knows the rule is there for good reasons.

Going through Nassau is a doddle, Don is an old hand. Mexico is rather more difficult. The city is over 7,000 feet above sea level, set in a bowl of mountains, some rising to over 15,000 feet. At night, the airport looks like a long black hole surrounded by the lights of the city. The hollow between the mountains traps the smog, reducing the visibility. And to make matters worse, the Spanish speaking air traffic controllers mangle the English language. It is a testing place if you are not used to it. Baird is not, but Don is. It all works out.

Late that evening, the three pilots relax in Plaza Garibaldi, surrounded by a cacophony of multiple Tijuana Brass bands, all playing different tunes at the same time. Don asks how he is enjoying being a captain. Baird says flying the aircraft is the easy bit, it's all the other things that are the problem. He is about to say more, but they are surrounded by yet another band drowning out all conversation.

'Tell you tomorrow,' he shouts.

Next morning, Baird sleeps in and goes down for a late breakfast. He finds Don there too.

'Can I say something to you — as a friend?'

'Of course,' says Baird.

'It's about Ivan. Do you know why he didn't come out with us last night?'

'Said he couldn't stand all that noise, getting old or something.'

'The real reason is he's very unhappy with your decisions going into Bermuda, says you pushed it too far. I did try to explain, but it would be better coming from you.'

'Well, what do you think?'

'Tight, but OK. You see,' he paused, 'You explained it the two of us — Geoff and me that is. But not enough to Ivan. He's not a navigator, the details escaped him.'

'OK,' sighs Baird, 'I'd better discuss it with him.'

'Take him through it all, just the two of you and let him have his say. Then emphasise all the safety margins you asked Geoff to build into his calculations. They were all correct. I know, because I checked them too.'

But next day the right opportunity seems always to escape him. That evening, going back through Nassau, the station manager comes aboard during the turn round and takes Baird to one side for a confidential briefing. 'There is a lady on board with a companion,' he says, 'they are travelling to London under assumed names. She is in the habit of booking economy seats and then, during the flight, demanding an upgrade to first class.' He hands Baird a signal from the Chairman saying she has tried this on too many times before. On no account should the captain allow this, even if she offers to pay the difference. 'Her real name is Georgiana, Principessa di Ponente, Duchess of Chulmleigh, but she is travelling as Mrs Chulmleigh. She is Italian married to an English Duke, and very conscious of her social position. She insists on being addressed as Your Royal Highness, which obviously she isn't, I'll leave it to you to decide what to call her.'

'Thanks a bunch.' Yet another problem, he thinks, first Ivan and now this. 'Which seats are they booked in?' 'Near the back.' He goes to find Guy to brief him too. 'Make sure you don't accede to her wishes, any problems call me.'

At top of climb, Guy comes up to say the lady is making a fuss. 'I've told her we are not allowed to upgrade her, but she won't take no for an answer. 'Tell the captain I wish to see him."

Baird goes back, with his cap on, so as to look more official. He finds Mrs Chulmleigh. She looks rather like Queen Mary, but younger and with very dark hair, dyed perhaps? Should he call her Madam, Your Grace or Your Royal Highness? Since she is supposed to be incognito, he decides on Madam. Her lady companion scolds him, saying she should be addressed as Your Royal Highness.

'I am so sorry, but it says here she is Mrs Chulmleigh.' Two can play at this game. 'Could you explain the problem, and I'll see if I can help.'

The Principessa looks grim. Her companion explains there must have been a mistake, Her Royal Highness always flies first class. A lady in the row behind puts down her magazine and cranes forward. Heads in front turn to listen.

'May I see your tickets?' Baird takes a look and lowers his voice. 'But these are economy, that is why you have been seated here.'

'But we asked for first class, some fool has put us back here.'

This goes on for a little while with Baird very politely and very quietly saying he does not have the authority to make the change.

The Principessa shushes him with a peremptory wave of her gloved hand. 'Now young man. You just listen to me. You,' she says pointedly, 'are supposed to be the captain. Be a man and make a decision.'

'But I have — already.'

'Not to my satisfaction. There is plenty of room in first class, you know it and I know it. I will have my people call your Chairman and tell him how ineffective you are.'

Baird replies, 'Thank you Madam. But I am duty bound to carry out his personal instructions. He says you have done this too many times before.'

'I don't think Her Royal Highness has been so insulted in all her life.'

Baird looks at the companion. How do I answer that? Guess I might as well be hung for a sheep as a lamb. He takes a deep breath and says, 'Madam, I would have thought a lady in her position would have known better. You must realise, I have no option other than to ask you please to stay in these seats. That is my last word.'

'You won't hear the last of this!' was her parting shot. As Baird turns to go, a distinguished looking gentleman on the other side of the aisle catches his eye, smiles, and gives him a quiet thumbs up.

'Silly old bag,' says Baird as he climbs back into his captain's seat.

'Well?' Asks Don, and Baird tells them what transpired. When they land in Bermuda, he hands over to the joining captain who is taking the aircraft on to London. He gives him the Chairman's signal and describes the lady in question, 'I'll talk to the station manager here too, in case she tries it on with him. Good luck!'

'Thanks, one storm goes away, and now you hand me another,' is the reply.

'Ruddy passengers,' Baird says to the others as they are driven to the hotel, and thinks to himself. And I have to talk to Ivan tomorrow. Tonight, I will just enjoy a few beers with the boys before going to bed. I've had enough for one day, and it's late. After five days of flying, much of it at night and with barely twenty-four hours rest at each stop, he wakes late, still feeling tired. Better find Ivan and talk it over before we set off back to London. What did I do wrong?

Baird finds him in the coffee shop having a late breakfast. 'May I join you?' He settles down opposite Ivan and orders a coffee. 'I'm not sure how I should start. Don says you weren't too happy about the flight into Bermuda. What went wrong?'

Ivan takes his time before saying, 'In my time, I've seen too many pilots make bad decisions. Some of them downright dangerous. You have the controls in front of you. I don't. You can do something about it. I can't. I'm not criticising, just telling you how it feels back there when you don't know what is going on.'

'But I thought I'd explained.'

'Look. You are all navigators, you know how to use the charts, work out distances and fuel requirements. You can size it up at a glance. I can't. Yes, you did tell me a little, but not enough. It would be like me showing you an electrical wiring diagram without explaining it. See what I mean? I know it all worked out, but at the time, I had to take it all on trust.'

'I'm sorry, what would you have liked me to show you?'

'You only had to ask Geoff to take me through the detail and the safety margins you asked him to build in. I know you had a lot on your mind. But remember your poor old engineer. He lives in a different world from all you young blokes. There's no need to explain it all now, Don has done all that. Here comes the waitress, you'd better order some breakfast before it's all off.'

'Thanks, Ivan. Guess I've still got a lot to learn.'

'Don't worry young fella, you'll do!'

◊◊◊

Back home, his wife greets him with a kiss, 'How did it go?'

Baird wearily puts down his briefcase and replies, 'The flying's OK, it's the people that are the problem.'

'You poor darling ... Oh, I almost forget, my mother's coming to lunch tomorrow. She asks that you pick her up from the station at ten.'

Love is in the Air

W e met an old friend of yours when we were in Australia.'

'Really, who was that?'

'Michael Boyd, sends his best wishes. Asks to be remembered to you.'

'I lost touch after he retired, often wondered where he ended up. What's he doing out there?'

'Lives there. Tuross Head, on the coast somewhere south of Sydney, says he was an old flying mate of yours.'

Fiona and David are old friends and neighbours here in Marlow, not far from the Thames. He is a solicitor and she's some kind of administrator in Wycombe Hospital. I've known them for years, the Australian trip was a treat for David's sixtieth birthday.

'Did you meet his wife, Wendy?'

'Yes, she said you'd know — they met on an aeroplane. That was how your name came up.'

I thought back to when I first met Michael Boyd in the winter of 1963, I was a new navigator then and he was a senior first officer. It was on a delightful trip to New York where we spent two weeks shuttling up and down between Idlewild, as it was then called, and Bermuda. BOAC used to station two Britannia crews in Manhattan, flying a shuttle on alternate days with a whole day off between each flight. It was easy flying and, after the drabness of England, the city was a revelation.

I remember Michael showing me the sights, Times Square, Stouffer's Top of the Sixes, watching the skaters at Rockefeller Centre, the Metropolitan Art Museum, Central Park — and low dives in Greenwich Village. One memorable evening we took the ferry across to Staten Island; the return voyage, with the lights from the skyscrapers shining out in the clear frosty air and reflecting on the Hudson, was stunning.

I flew with him again in '66, by that time we were on VC10s. The trip was to Karachi with a clear day off in Beirut on the way out, and again, on the return flight back to London. Beirut in summer was yet another revelation. Before the civil war, it was an elegant city with French style villas dating from the days of the Mandate. Our hotel stood on the Corniche facing the sea. Behind, in the city itself, there were wide boulevards lined with high rise buildings and modern shops, exciting narrow back streets, busy Arab souks and little restaurants serving Middle Eastern mezzes.

Round the headland towards the harbour, pretty girls sunbathed on the beach by Saint

Georges Hotel and Yacht Club. What more could a young man want? But we only had time for a gentle walk round the city and an evening in the rather sleazy Golden Bar where airline crews from many companies used to meet and drink.

Three days later, on the way back from Karachi, with a whole clear day at our disposal, Michael decided we should rent a taxi and go over the mountains to Baalbek. And quite an adventure it was too — up twisty mountain roads and down into the fertile Beqaa valley to see the Temple of Jupiter, the largest in the Roman world. Back in the city that evening, he suggested we round the day off with dinner in a little French restaurant washed down with a good Chateau Musar wine. Michael knew Beirut well.

David interrupted, 'Doesn't look as though you did much flying, sounds more like a holiday to me. Where does Wendy come into all this?'

'I'm coming to that, but I wanted you to know what Michael was like — energetic, adventurous, curious, cultured, and a man of great charm.'

The next time our paths crossed, some years later, he was now a captain and a changed man. He was still pleasant enough, but the sense of fun had gone, something must have happened in his life. I thought it unlikely to be the weight of command, he did not seem that sort of a man, although I knew several pilots who had been much changed by the extra responsibility; surely this hadn't happened to Michael. But it wasn't the moment to ask — just get on with the job, I thought, there will be ample time to find out if he wants to talk. There isn't much you don't learn about your companions on a long two week trip, and this one was all the way to Sydney with stops in New York, Los Angeles, Honolulu and Fiji, and then back the same way to London.

I didn't see him in New York, but that isn't unusual as captains stayed in superior hotels away from the rest of the crew. In Los Angeles, several of us met up one evening for dinner. Michael remained quiet, barely engaging in the normal chit chat. It was not until we were in Honolulu that he opened up a bit. We had gone for a walk in the cool of the evening and, after a while, had stopped for a beer. We found a place well away from the tourist hot spots where, apart from us two and the barman, the bar was almost empty. After the first few sips, Michael ran a finger up and down the moisture on the outside of his glass and fiddled with the beer mat. His normally alert face was sad, his gaze fixed upon the patterns he was making in the water that dribbled down and was now spreading on the table.

'Want to tell me about it?'

'I'm sorry. I really must snap out of it. It's just that ...' After a long pause, 'Last year I lost my wife.' And said no more. I was about to ask when he raised his hand to still me, it was clearly something that still distressed him deeply. I looked with sympathy at his brooding eyes, the furrows that had once been laughter lines, the slump of his shoulders and his greying hair. He had not been like that when I first knew him. Neither was he like that on the aeroplane, he knew how to hold himself together in public and when flying, but not so well now we were alone. There was little I could do to help other than offer him another beer which he refused. We talked about something else and then strolled back to the hotel.

Next evening, we left Honolulu at the ungodly hour of 11.30 pm bound for Nadi (pronounced Nandi), seven hours away in Fiji. His Captain Boyd persona was back in place, slightly aloof and sternly in command. He gave his usual 'welcome aboard' spiel to the passengers, ending with the suggestion that, if anyone on board was celebrating their birthday, they had better make the most of it, because it would end when we crossed the International Date Line in five hours' time.

There is very little to see in the vastness of the Pacific Ocean at night. Only the stars to keep you company and a few uninhabited islands passing unseen below. Half an hour before crossing the Date Line, with still another two hours to go to Fiji, the welcome appearance of Babs, one of the stewardesses, broke the monotony. She burst in waving a birthday card the cabin crew had cobbled up from a first class menu. It was magnificently decorated with details of the flight and a drawing of our VC10 with a caricature of Michael sitting high on the tail, holding reins that led forward to the cockpit. They had all signed it, as had many of the passengers, wishing a lady passenger a Very Happy Birthday from everyone on board, 'would the captain sign it too please?'

'Certainly not,' he said. Oh dear, I thought that didn't sound like the Michael I knew of old. Then he added, 'Not until I've seen her, bring her up.'

The lady in question was ushered into the cockpit where Michael invited her to sit in the jump seat. He then rang the call bell and, right on cue, the chief steward appeared with a glass of champagne. This was a little more like it. We all wished Wendy — that was her name — a happy birthday, claimed a kiss, and signed the card. She turned out to be an Australian on her way home to Sydney after a business meeting in the US. She had dark hair flicked up around her cheekbones, gorgeous brown eyes and a bubbly personality. The champagne perhaps? Unfortunately, the four of us could not indulge, but she enjoyed another. I could see Michael was impressed.

She made the usual comments about how complicated everything looked, giving him the opportunity to explain the way some of the dials, levers and switches worked. Then he asked if she would like to come up for the landing into Nadi. In fact, she was so interested and Michael so animated that she stayed for the rest of the flight until after we shut down the engines in front of the terminal building. We explained we would be staying in Fiji, while a new crew would take the aircraft on to Sydney. Michael sympathised on the shortness of her birthday, and no one was so impolite as to inquire how old she was, but I would guess mid-thirties.

Next day, we continued to Sydney where we had three days off, and I can tell you, after six days of flying, much of it through the night, and now half way round the world, we needed the break. But even short of sleep and ten hours out of synch with local time, it did not stop us from going out on the town. We saw little of Michael, he said he had friends to visit.

Five months later and quite out of the blue, I received an invitation to the wedding of Wendy Susan Fogarty to Michael Richard Boyd out in Australia, but how was I to get out to Sydney on the appointed date? With great regret, I declined their kind invitation, but wrote to Michael to express my happiness for him. No problem, they replied, there would be another celebration in the UK for those who couldn't make it to Australia.

◊◊◊

The Oatlands Park Hotel is a converted Tudor house built and remodelled several times over on the site of an ancient royal palace. It lies on the outskirts of Weybridge, in a secluded park away from the bustle of suburban life, but conveniently close to London Airport. It was here that Michael and Wendy decided to invite some fifty or so of their friends and colleagues. Wendy had especially invited some of the crew of that flight to Fiji who had sparked things off for them — Babs whose idea it had been to organise the card, Graham, the chief steward who gave Wendy the champagne, Don, our flight engineer, and Adrian, the steward, who had trained as a commercial artist before chucking it in to go flying. It was he who had drawn the impromptu birthday card, and now he had been persuaded by Wendy to draw the invitation and place cards for the occasion.

And what a great party it was. What really pleased me was the transformation Wendy had wrought on Michael. When someone played the newly released song, Love is in the Air by John Paul Young, Babs even persuaded him to sing along too.

◊◊◊

The next time I flew with Michael, he was a senior captain and, as I would soon be coming up for my own command course, he suggested I do most of the flying. The trip was out to Panama via Bermuda and Kingston, Jamaica. After the shuttle to Panama, we had two days off in Morgan's. Harbour, the little hotel in Port

Royal where we stayed when flying through Kingston. It is a relaxed sort of place with an open air bar overlooking the swimming pool and the harbour.

The BOAC sports recreation club kept a small sailing dinghy there for our use. Michael, in his usual way, suggested we take it out to Lime Cay, a few miles out to sea. We loaded up with sandwiches and cans of Red Stripe beer from the hotel and went out for the day. The little island is scarcely 400 yards long and less than 100 wide, merely a low lying strip of coral and sand. Fortunately, there are some scrubby looking trees. We relaxed in their shade and I asked him about Wendy.

'She's OK,' he replied, rolling over in the sand without spilling his beer, 'More than OK really. Actually, very happy.'

The leaves of the mangroves rustled in the wind, small waves swished up the shallow sloping beach. I waited for him to say more. He remained quiet.

'We wondered where you went in Sydney,' I remarked. 'Only a fleeting glimpse as you left the Menzies, then nothing until pickup.' I waited, 'Cherchez la femme, perhaps?'

'Oh, alright, yes. I knew she had an apartment in Kirribilli, Babs told me. I had to search the phone book. I knew her name from the passenger list, so it wasn't too hard.' Was he slightly pink, or was it sunburn? I raised an eyebrow and said nothing.

'Oh — well, you might as well know. I phoned

her, had to try several times, she was out most of the day. But I plucked up courage and asked her out to dinner — The Oyster Bar on Circular Quay was her choice.' Long pause. 'It's only a ten minute walk down from the Menzies Hotel.

'I met her off the ferry, it was warm, no wind, and ordered up two glasses of champagne to remind her of her visit to the cockpit. D'you know the place? Near the opera house with a fabulous view across the water towards the bridge. We stayed talking until late.'

Yes, I told him, I knew the Oyster Bar well — Sydney rock oysters, grilled mahi mahi, a chilled sauvignon blanc, a soft warm night, I couldn't think of a better place to woo a lady.

'Next day, I went over to Kirribilli and she suggested a ferry trip around some of the inlets further inland. No idea where we went,' adding shyly, 'I suppose I really only had eyes for Wendy. Three months later, I asked her if she'd like to marry me.'

'Bit difficult all the way from London, wasn't it?'

'She came to London on another of her business trips, and we met up for one evening. That was all we could manage. I had some leave coming up, what if I came out to Sydney? And when I was there, I proposed. Best thing I ever did.'

'In the Oyster Bar?'

He smiled sheepishly.

When we parted in London at the end of the trip, I thanked him for all the help and advice he had given me when I was doing the flying.

'You ought to become a training captain.'

'Not bloody likely. I'm enjoying life too much.'

I didn't relate all these details to Fiona and David, but they got the message. It's amazing what the love of a good woman can do for a man.

Also from SunRise

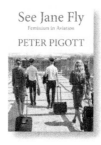

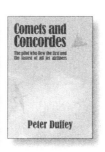

Printed in Great Britain
by Amazon

87359598R00142